BILLY BUDD, FORETOPMAN

BY HERMAN MELVILLE

with special aids prepared by
Hart Day Leavitt

BANTAM  BOOKS

BANTAM PATHFINDER EDITIONS
NEW YORK / TORONTO / LONDON

RLI:
VLM 9.0
IL 9.12

▰

BILLY BUDD, FORETOPMAN

A Bantam Pathfinder edition / published May 1965
2nd printing
3rd printing
4th printing
5th printing

ACKNOWLEDGMENTS

Howard, Leon. From *Herman Melville: A Biography. Reprinted by permission of the University of California Press.*

Mumford, Lewis. From *Herman Melville. Reprinted by permission of Harcourt, Brace & World, Inc.*

Humphreys, A. R. From *Herman Melville. Copyright © 1962 by A. R. Humphreys. Reprinted by permission of Grove Press, Inc., Oliver & Boyd Ltd. and A. R. Humphreys.*

Portions of a letter from Robert Frost to Lawrance Thompson reprinted from *Selected Letters of Robert Frost edited by Lawrance Thompson. Copyright © 1964 by Holt, Rinehart and Winston, Inc. Reprinted by permission of the Estate of Robert Frost and by Holt, Rinehart and Winston, Inc.*

Kael, Pauline. "*Peter Ustinov's Billy Budd,*" FILM QUARTERLY. © 1963 by The Regents of the University of California. *Reprinted from* FILM QUARTERLY, *Vol. XVI, No. 3, pp. 53–56, by permission of The Regents. Also reprinted by permission of Pauline Kael.*

Fuller, Edmund. From *Mutiny. Copyright, 1953, by Crown Publishers, Inc. Reprinted by permission of the publisher.*

Miller, James. From *Reader's Guide. Reprinted by permission of Farrar, Straus & Giroux, Inc.*

Freeman, John. From *Herman Melville. Copyright, 1936, by The Macmillan Company.*

Thompson, Lawrance. From *Melville's Quarrel with God. Reprinted by permission of Princeton University Press. Copyright, 1952, by Princeton University Press.*

Library of Congress Catalog Card Number: 65–17433

Bantam Books are published by Bantam Books, Inc., a subsidiary of Grosset & Dunlap, Inc. Its trade-mark, consisting of the words "Bantam Books" and the portrayal of a bantam, is registered in the United States Patent Office and in other countries. Marca Registrada. Bantam Books, Inc., 271 Madison Avenue, New York, N. Y. 10016

PRINTED IN THE UNITED STATES OF AMERICA

For the reader's enjoyment and understanding, this new Pathfinder edition includes the following special features:

"Clues to Understanding the Mysteries in BILLY BUDD"—An illuminating guide that (A) summarizes the story; (B) sketches the allusions; (C) points up omissions; (D) outlines the major issues and their effects.

Sources and Environment—The power of rules in the ninteenth century; the author's own navy experiences; a similar case that involved Melville's cousin; the Spithead and Nore mutinies.

BILLY BUDD and THE CAINE MUTINY—Both sea stories develop the tragic conflict between an individual and a massive institution.

Opinions, Reviews, and Comments—A sampling of critical opinion with provocative interpretations and insights into the novel.

A biographical sketch of Herman Melville.

Hart Day Leavitt, the editor, has taught English at Phillips Academy, Andover, since 1937. He is also co-author of STOP, LOOK AND WRITE! Effective Writing through Pictures.

BANTAM PATHFINDER EDITIONS

Bantam Pathfinder Editions provide the best in
fiction and nonfiction in a wide variety of
subject areas. They include novels by classic
and contemporary writers; vivid, accurate
histories and biographies; authoritative works
in the sciences; collections of short
stories, plays and poetry.

Bantam Pathfinder Editions are carefully
selected and approved. They are durably bound,
printed on specially selected high-quality paper,
and presented in a new and handsome format.

Contents

A NOTE ON THE TEXT

The text for this edition, prepared by the noted Mr. William Plomer in the edition published by John Lehmann Ltd. in 1946, is basically the same as the versions that have been universally available during the past forty years.

Recent studies of Melville's papers indicate that if he had ever prepared a final manuscript, it would have been somewhat different from the texts known to most readers. A new version of the novel based on these studies is now available (University of Chicago Press, edited by Harrison Hayford and Merton M. Sealts, Jr.). Sometime in the future, perhaps, this version may become standard.

The present editor and publisher have decided to follow the conventional text for two reasons: the new discoveries involve matters of scholarship that are beyond the scope of most readers and students; and these discoveries have not yet been fully assessed and assimilated even by the scholarly community.

PART ONE

Billy Budd, Foretopman
(An inside narrative)

What befell him
in the year of the
Great Mutiny etc.

Dedicated to
JACK CHASE
ENGLISHMAN
wherever that great heart may now be
here on earth or harboured in Paradise.
Captain of the Maintop in the year 1843
in the U.S. Frigate *United States*.

PREFACE

The year 1797, the year of this narrative, belongs to a period which, as every thinker now feels, involved a crisis for Christendom, not exceeded in its undetermined momentousness at the time by any other era whereof there is record. The opening proposition made by the Spirit of that Age, involved a rectification of the Old World's hereditary wrongs. In France, to some extent, this was bloodily effected. But what then? Straightway the Revolution itself became a wrongdoer, one more oppressive than the kings. Under Napoleon it enthroned upstart kings, and initiated that prolonged agony of continual war whose final throe was Waterloo. During those years not the wisest could have foreseen that the outcome of all would be what to some thinkers apparently it has since turned out to be, a political advance along nearly the whole line for Europeans.

Now, as elsewhere hinted, it was something caught from the Revolutionary Spirit that at Spithead emboldened the man-of-war's men to rise against real abuses, long-standing ones, and afterwards at the Nore to make inordinate and aggressive demands, successful resistance to which was confirmed only when the ringleaders were hung for an admonitory spectacle to the anchored fleet. Yet in a way analogous to the operation of the Revolution at large, the

Great Mutiny, though by Englishmen naturally deemed monstrous at the time, doubtless gave the first latent prompting to most important reforms in the British Navy.

I

(*An inside Narrative*)

In the time before steamships, or then more frequently than now, a stroller along the docks of any considerable seaport would occasionally have his attention arrested by a group of bronzed marines, man-of-war's men or merchant sailors in holiday attire ashore on liberty. In certain instances they would flank, or, like a bodyguard, quite surround some superior figure of their own class, moving along with them like Aldebaran amongst the lesser lights of his constellation. That signal object was the "Handsome Sailor" of the less prosaic time alike of the military and merchant navies. With no perceptible trace of the vainglorious about him, rather with the offhand unaffectedness of natural regality, he seemed to accept the spontaneous homage of his shipmates. A somewhat remarkable instance recurs to me. In Liverpool, now half a century ago, I saw under the shadow of the great dingy street-wall of Prince's Dock (an obstruction long since removed) a common sailor, so intensely black that he must needs have been a native African of the unadulterate blood of Ham. A symmetric figure much above the average height. The two ends of a gay silk handkerchief thrown loose about the neck danced upon the displayed ebony of his chest; in his ears were big hoops of gold, and a Scotch Highland bonnet with a tartan band set off his shapely head.

It was a hot noon in July; and his face, lustrous with perspiration, beamed with barbaric good-humour. In jovial sallies right and left, his white teeth flashing into view, he rollicked along, the centre of a company of his shipmates. These were made up of such an assortment of tribes and complexions as would have well fitted them to be marched up by Anacharsis Cloots before the bar of the first French Assembly as Representatives of the Human

Race. At each spontaneous tribute rendered by the way-
farers to this black pagod of a fellow—the tribute of a
pause and stare, and less frequent in exclamation—the
motley retinue showed that they took that sort of pride in
the evoker of it which the Assyrian priests doubtless
showed for their grand sculptured Bull when the faithful
prostrated themselves. To return——

If in some cases a bit of a nautical Murat in setting
forth his person ashore, the Handsome Sailor of the period
in question evinced nothing of the dandified Billy-be-Dam,
an amusing character all but extinct now, but occasionally
to be encountered, and in a form yet more amusing than
the original, at the tiller of the boats on the tempestuous
Erie Canal or, more likely, vapouring in the groggeries
along the tow-path. Invariably a proficient in his perilous
calling, he was also more or less of a mighty boxer or
wrestler. He was strength and beauty. Tales of his prowess
were recited. Ashore he was the champion, afloat the
spokeman; on every suitable occasion always foremost.
Close-reefing topsails in a gale, there he was, astride the
weather yard-arm-end, foot in "stirrup," both hands tug-
ging at the "ear-ring" as at a bridle, in very much the
attitude of young Alexander curbing the fiery Bucephalus.
A superb figure, tossed up as by the horns of Taurus
against the thunderous sky, cheerily ballooning to the
strenuous file along the spar.

The moral nature was seldom out of keeping with the
physical make. Indeed, except as toned by the former,
the comeliness and power, always attractive in masculine
conjunction, hardly could have drawn the sort of homage
the Handsome Sailor in some examples received from his
less gifted associates.

Such a cynosure, at least in aspect, and something such
too in nature, though with important variations made apparent as the story proceeds, was welkin-eyed Billy Budd—
or Baby Budd, as more familiarly, under circumstances
hereafter to be given, he at last came to be called—aged
twenty-one, a foretopman of the fleet toward the close of
the last decade of the eighteenth century. It was not very
long prior to the time of the narration that follows that he

had entered the King's Service, having been impressed on
the Narrow Seas from a homeward-bound English merchantman into a seventy-four outward-bound, H.M.S.
Indomitable; which ship, as was not unusual in those
hurried days, had been obliged to put to sea short of her
proper complement of men. Plump upon Billy at first sight
in the gangway the boarding-officer, Lieutenant Ratcliffe,
pounced, even before the merchantman's crew formally
was mustered on the quarter-deck for his deliberate inspec-
tion. And him only he selected. For whether it was because
the other men when ranged before him showed to ill
advantage after Billy, or whether he had some scruples in
view of the merchantman being rather short-handed; however it might be, the officer contented himself with his first
spontaneous choice. To the surprise of the ship's company,
though much to the Lieutenant's satisfaction, Billy made
no demur. But indeed any demur would have been as idle
as the protest of a goldfinch popped into a cage.

Noting this uncomplaining acquiescence, all but cheerful one might say, the shipmates turned a surprised glance
of silent reproach at the sailor. The shipmaster was one of
those worthy mortals found in every vocation, even the
humbler ones—the sort of person whom everybody agrees
in calling "a respectable man." And—nor so strange to
report as it may appear to be—though a ploughman of
the troubled waters, life-long contending with the intrac-
table elements, there was nothing this honest soul at heart
loved better than simple peace and quiet. For the rest, he
was fifty or thereabouts, a little inclined to corpulence, a
prepossessing face, unwhiskered, and of an agreeable
colour, a rather full face, humanely intelligent in expression. On a fair day with a fair wind and all going well, a
certain musical chime in his voice seemed to be the veritable unobstructed outcome of the innermost man. He had
much prudence, much conscientiousness, and there were
occasions when these virtues were the cause of overmuch
disquietude in him. On a passage, so long as his craft
was in any proximity to land, no sleep for Captain Graveling. He took to heart those serious responsibilities not so
heavily borne by some shipmasters.

Now while Billy Budd was down in forecastle getting his kit together, the *Indomitable's* lieutenant, burly and bluff, nowise disconcerted by Captain Graveling's omitting to proffer the customary hospitalities on an occasion so unwelcome to him, an omission simply caused by preoccupation of thought, unceremoniously invited himself into the cabin, and also to a flask from the spirit locker, a receptacle which his experienced eye instantly discovered. In fact, he was one of those sea-dogs in whom all the hardship and peril of naval life in the great prolonged wars of his time never impaired the natural instinct for sensuous enjoyment. His duty he always faithfully did; but duty is sometimes a dry obligation, and he was for irrigating its aridity whensoever possible with a fertilising decoction of strong waters. For the cabin's proprietor there was nothing left but to play the part of the enforced host with whatever grace and alacrity were practicable. As necessary adjuncts to the flasks, he silently placed tumbler and water-jug before the irrepressible guest. But excusing himself from partaking just then, dismally watched the unembarrassed officer deliberately diluting his grog a little, then tossing it off in three swallows, pushing the empty tumbler away, yet not so far as to be beyond easy reach, at the same time settling himself in his seat, and smacking his lips with high satisfaction, looking straight at the host.

These proceedings over, the Master broke the silence; and there lurked a rueful reproach in the tone of his voice: "Lieutenant, you are going to take my best man from me, the jewel of 'em."

"Yes, I know," rejoined the other, immediately drawing back the tumbler, preliminary to a replenishing; "yes, I know. Sorry."

"Beg pardon, but you don't understand, Lieutenant. See here now. Before I shipped that young fellow, my forecastle was a rat-pit of quarrels. It was black times, I tell you, aboard the *Rights* here. I was worried to that degree of pipe had no comfort for me. But Billy came; and it was like a Catholic priest striking peace in an Irish shindy. Not that he preached to them or said or did anything in particular; but a virtue went out of him, sugaring

Freedom of
inherent
thinking ←

the sour ones. They took to him like hornets to treacle;
all but the bluffer of the gang, the big, shaggy chap with the
fire-red whiskers. He indeed, out of envy, perhaps, of the
newcomer, and thinking such a 'sweet and pleasant fellow,'
as he mockingly designated him to the others, could hardly
have the spirit of a game-cock, must needs bestir himself
in trying to get up an ugly row with him. Billy forbore with
him, and reassured with him in a pleasant way—he is something like myself, Lieutenant, to whom aught like a quarrel
is hateful—but nothing served. So, in the second dog-watch
one day the Red Whiskers, in presence of the others, under
pretence of showing Billy just whence a sirloin steak was
cut—for the fellow had once been a butcher—insultingly
gave him a dig under the ribs. Quick as lightning Billy let
fly his arm. I dare say he never meant to do quite as much
as he did, but anyhow he gave the burly fool a terrible
drubbing. It took about half a minute, I should think. And,
Lord bless you, the lubber was astonished at the celerity.
And will you believe it, Lieutenant, the Red Whiskers now
really loves Billy—loves him, or is the biggest hypocrite
that ever I heard of. But they all love him. Some of 'em
do his washing, darn old trousers for him; the carpenter
is at odd times making a pretty little chest of drawers for
him. Anybody will do anything for Billy Budd; and it's the
happy family here. Now, Lieutenant, if that young fellow
goes, I know how it will be aboard the *Rights*. Not again
very soon shall I, coming up from dinner, lean over the
capstan smoking a quiet pipe—no, not very soon again,
I think. Ay, Lieutenant, you are going to take away the
jewel of 'em; you are going to take away my peacemaker."
And with that the good soul had really some ado in check-
ing a rising sob.

"Well," said the Lieutenant, who had listened with
amused interest to all this, and now waxing merry with
his tipple, "well, blessed are the peacemakers, especially
the fighting peacemakers! And such are the seventy-four
beauties, some of which you see poking their noses out of
the port-holes of yonder warship lying-to for me," pointing through the cabin windows at the *Indomitable*. "But
courage! don't look so downhearted, man. Why, I pledge

you in advance the royal approbation. Rest assured that His Majesty will be delighted to know that in time when his hardtack is not sought for by sailors with such avidity as should be; a time also when some shipmasters privily resent the borrowing from them of a tar or two for the service; His Majesty, I say, will be delighted to learn that *one* shipmaster at least cheerfully surrenders to the King the flower of his flock, a sailor who with equal loyalty makes no dissent. But where's my Beauty? Ah," looking through the cabin's open door, "here he comes; and, by Jove! lugging along his chest—Apollo with his portmanteau! My man," stepping out to him, "you can't take that big box aboard a warship. The boxes there are mostly shot-boxes. Put your duds in a bag, lad. Boot and saddle for the cavalryman, bag and hammock for the man-of-war's man."

The transfer from chest to bag was made. And, after seeing his man into the cutter, and then following him down, the Lieutenant pushed off from the *Rights-of-Man.* That was the merchant ship's name; though by her master and crew abbreviated in sailor fashion into the *Rights.* The hard-headed Dundee owner was a staunch admirer of Thomas Paine, whose book in rejoinder to Burke's arraignment of the French Revolution had then been published for some time, and had gone everywhere. In christening his vessel after the title of Paine's volume, the man of Dundee was something like his contemporary shipowner, Stephen Girard of Philadelphia, whose sympathies alike with his native land and its liberal philosophies he evinced by naming his ships after Voltaire, Diderot, and so forth.

But now when the boat swept under the merchantman's stern, and officer and oarsmen were noting, some bitterly and others with a grin, the name emblazoned there; just then it was that the new recruit jumped up from the bow where the coxswain had directed him to sit, and, waving his hat to his silent shipmates sorrowfully looking over at him from the taffrail, bade the lads a genial good-bye. Then making a salutation as to the ship herself, "And good-bye to you too, old *Rights-of-Man!*"

"Down, sir," roared the Lieutenant, instantly assuming all the rigour of his rank, though with difficulty repressing a smile.

To be sure, Billy's action was a terrible breach of naval decorum. But in that decorum he had never been instructed; in consideration of which the Lieutenant would hardly have been so energetic in reproof but for the concluding farewell to the ship. This he rather took as meant to convey a covert sally on the new recruit's part, a sly slur at impressment in general, and that of himself in especial. And yet, more likely, if satire it was in effect, it was hardly so by intention, for Billy, though happily endowed with the gaiety of high health, youth, and a free heart, was yet by no means of a satirical turn. The will to it and the sinister dexterity were alike wanting. To deal in double meaning and insinuations of any sort was quite foreign to his nature.

As to his enforced enlistment, that he seemed to take pretty much as he was wont to take any vicissitudes of weather. Like the animals, though no philosopher he was, without knowing it, practically a fatalist. And, it may be, that he rather liked this adventurous turn in his affairs which promised an opening into novel scenes and martial excitements.

Aboard the *Indomitable* our merchant-sailor was forthwith rated as an able seaman, and assigned to the starboard watch of the foretop. He was soon at home in the service, not at all disliked for his unpretentious good looks, and a sort of genial happy-go-lucky air. No merrier man in his mess; in marked contrast to certain other individuals included like himself among the impressed portion of the ship's company; for these when not actively employed were sometimes, and more particularly in the last dog-watch, when the drawing near of twilight induced reverie, apt to fall into a saddish mood which in some partook of sullenness. But they were not so young as our foretopman, and no few of them must have known a hearth of some sort, others may have had wives and children left, too probably, in uncertain circumstances, and hardly any but must have acknowledged kith and kin; while for Billy, as will shortly be seen, his entire family was practically invested in himself.

II

center of attraction

incense—christ figure

Though our new-made foretopman was well received in the top and on the gun-decks, hardly here was he that cynosure he had previously been among those minor ships' companies of the merchant marine, with which companies only had he hitherto consorted.

He was young; and despite his all but fully developed frame, in aspect looked even younger than he really was. This was owing to a lingering adolescent expression in the as yet smooth face, all but feminine in purity of natural complexion, but where, thanks to his sea-going, the lily was quite suppressed, and the rose had some ado visibly to flush through the tan.

To one essentially such a novice in the complexities of factitious life, the abrupt transition from his former and simpler sphere to the ampler and more knowing world of a great warship—this might well have abashed him had there been any conceit or vanity in his composition. Among her miscellaneous multitude, the *Indomitable* mustered several individuals who, however inferior in grade, were of no common natural stamp, sailors more signally susceptive of that air which continuous martial discipline and repeated presence in battle can in some degree impart even to the average man. As the *Handsome Sailor* Billy Budd's position aboard the seventy-four was something analogous to that of a rustic beauty transplanted from the provinces and brought into competition with the high-born dames of the court. But this change of circumstances he scarce noted. As little did he observe that something about him provoked an ambiguous smile in one or two harder faces among the blue-jackets. Nor less unaware was he of the peculiar favourable effect his person and demeanour had upon the more intelligent gentlemen of the quarter-deck.

Welkin blue—sky

Nor could this well have been otherwise. Cast in a mould
peculiar to the finest physical examples of those Englishmen in whom the Saxon strain would seem not at all to
partake of any Norman or other admixture, he showed in
face that humane look of reposeful good-nature which
the Greek sculptor in some instances gave to his heroic
strong man, Hercules. But this again was subtly modified
by another and pervasive quality. The ear, small and
shapely, the arch of the foot, the curve in mouth and nos-
tril, even the indurated hand dyed to the orange-tawny of
the toucan's bill, a hand telling of the halyards and tar-
buckets; but, above all, something in the mobile expression, and every chance attitude and movement, something
suggestive of a mother eminently favoured by Love and
the Graces; all this strangely indicated a lineage in direct
contradiction to his lot. The mysteriousness here, became
less mysterious through a matter of fact elicited when
Billy at the capstan was being formally mustered into the
service. Asked by the officer, a small, brisk little gentleman as it chanced, among other questions, his place of
birth, he replied, "Please, sir, I don't know."

"Don't you know where you were born? Who was your
father?"

"God knows, sir."

Struck by the straightforward simplicity of these replies, the officer next asked, "Do you know anything
about your beginning?"

"No, sir. But I have heard that I was found in a pretty
silk-lined basket hanging one morning from the knocker of
a good man's door in Bristol."

"*Found,* say you? Well," throwing back his head, and
looking up and down the new recruit—"well, it turns out
to have been a pretty good find. Hope they'll find some
more like you, my man; the fleet sadly needs them."

Yes, Billy Budd was a foundling, a presumable by-
blow, and, evidently, no ignoble one. Noble descent was
as evident in him as in a blood horse.

For the rest, with little or no sharpness of faculty or any
trace of the wisdom of the serpent, nor yet quite a dove,
he possessed a certain degree of intelligence along with

the unconventional rectitude of a sound human creature—
one to whom not yet has been proffered the questionable
apple of knowledge. He was illiterate; he could not read,
but he could sing, and like the illiterate nightingale was
sometimes the composer of his own song.

Of self-consciousness he seemed to have little or none,
or about as much as we may reasonably impute to a dog
of St. Bernard's breed.

Habitually being with the elements and knowing little
more of the land than as a beach, or, rather, that portion
of the terraqueous globe providentially set apart for dance-
houses, doxies and tapsters, in short, what sailors call a
"fiddlers' green," his simple nature remained unsophisticated by those moral obliquities which are not in every
case incomparable with that manufacturable thing known
as respectability. But are sailor frequenters of fiddlers'
greens without vices? No; but less often than with landsmen do their vices, so-called, partake of crookedness of
heart, seeming less to proceed from viciousness than ex-
uberance of vitality after long restraint, frank manifestations in accordance with natural law. By his original
constitution, aided by the co-operating influences of his
lot, Billy in many respects was little more than a sort of
upright barbarian, much such perhaps as Adam presumably might have been ere the urbane Serpent wriggled himself into his company.

And here be it submitted that, apparently going to cor-
roborate the doctrine of man's fall (a doctrine now popularly ignored), it is observable that where certain virtues
pristine and unadulterate peculiarly characterise anybody
in the external uniform of civilisation, they will upon scrutiny seem not to be derived from custom or convention
but rather to be out of keeping with these, as if indeed
exceptionally transmitted from a period prior to Cain's
city and citified man. The character marked by such qualities has to an unvitiated taste an untampered-with flavour
like that of berries, while the man thoroughly civilised, even
in a fair specimen of the breed, has to the same moral
palate a questionable smack as of a compounded wine. To
any stray inheritor of these primitive qualities found, like

Caspar Hauser, wandering dazed in any Christian capital of our time, the poet's famous invocation, near two thousand years ago, of the good rustic out of his latitude in the Rome of the Caesars, still appropriately holds:—

> "Faithful in word and thought,
> What has Thee, Fabian, to the city brought?"

Though our Handsome Sailor had as much of masculine beauty as one can expect anywhere to see; nevertheless, like the beautiful woman in one of Hawthorne's minor tales, there was just one thing amiss in him. No visible blemish, indeed, as with the lady; no, but an occasional liability to a vocal defect. Though in the hour of elemental uproar or peril, he was everything that a sailor should be, yet under sudden provocation of strong heart-feeling his voice, otherwise singularly musical, as if expressive of the harmony within, was apt to develop an organic hesitancy,—in fact, more or less of a stutter or even worse. In this particular Billy was a striking instance that the arch-interpreter, the envious marplot of Eden, still has more or less to do with every human consignment to this planet of earth. In every case, one way or another, he is sure to slip in his little card, as much as to remind us—I too have a hand here.

The avowal of such an imperfection in the Handsome Sailor should be evidence not alone that he is not presented as a conventional hero, but also that the story in which he is the main figure is no romance.

III

At the time of Billy Budd's arbitrary enlistment into the *Indomitable* that ship was on her way to join the Mediterranean fleet. No long time elapsed before the junction was effected. As one of that fleet the seventy-four participated in its movements, though at times on account of her superior sailing qualities, in the absence of frigates, dispatched on separate duty as a scout, and at times on less temporary service. But with all this the story has little concernment, restricted as it is to the inner life of one particular ship and the career of an individual sailor.

It was the summer of 1797. In the April of that year had occurred the commotion at Spithead, followed in May by a second and yet more serious outbreak in the fleet at the Nore. The latter is known, and without exaggeration in the epithet, as the Great Mutiny. It was indeed a demonstration more menacing to England than the contemporary manifestos and conquering and proselytising armies of the French Directory.

To the Empire, the Nore Mutiny was what a strike in the fire-brigade would be to London threatened by general arson. In a crisis when the Kingdom might well have anticipated the famous signal that some years later published along the naval line of battle what it was that upon occasion England expected of Englishmen; *that* was the time when at the mast-heads of the three-deckers and seventy-fours moored in her own roadstead—a fleet, the right arm of a Power then all but the sole free conservative one of the Old World, the blue-jackets, to be numbered by thousands, ran up with hurrahs the British colours with the union and cross wiped out; by that cancellation transmuting the flag of founded law and freedom defined, into the enemy's red meteor of unbridled and unbounded revolt. Reasonable discontent growing out of practical grievances in the fleet had been ignited into irrational combustion as by live cinders blown across the Channel from France in flames.

The event converted into irony for a time those spirited strains of Dibdin—as a song-writer no mean auxiliary to the English Government—at this European conjuncture, strains celebrating, among other things, the patriotic devotion of the British tar—

"And as for my life, 'tis the King's!"

Such an episode in the Island's grand naval story her naval historians naturally abridge; one of them (G. P. R. James) candidly acknowledging that fain would he pass it over did not "impartiality forbid fastidiousness." And yet his mention is less a narration than a reference, having to do hardly at all with details. Nor are these readily to be found in the libraries. Like some other events in every age befalling States everywhere, including America, the Great Mutiny was of such character that national pride along with views of policy would fain shade it off into the historical background. Such events cannot be ignored, but there is a considerate way of historically treating them. If a well-constituted individual refrains from blazoning aught amiss or calamitous in his family, a nation in the like circumstances may without reproach be equally discreet.

Though after parleyings between Government and the ringleaders, and concessions by the former as to some glaring abuses, the first uprising—that at Spithead—with difficulty was put down, or matters for a time pacified; yet at the Nore the unforeseen renewal of insurrection on a yet larger scale, and emphasised in the conferences that ensued by demands deemed by the authorities not only inadmissible but aggressively insolent, indicated, if the red flag did not sufficiently do so, what was the spirit animating the men. Final suppression, however, there was; but only made possible perhaps by the unswerving loyalty of the marine corps, and a voluntary resumption of loyalty among influential sections of the crews. To some extent the Nore Mutiny may be regarded as analogous to the distempering irruption of contagious fever in a frame constitutionally sound, and which anon throws it off.

At all events, among these thousands of mutineers were some of the tars who not so very long afterwards—whether wholly prompted thereto by patriotism, or pugnacious instinct, or by both—helped to win a coronet for Nelson at the Nile, and the naval crown of crowns for him at Trafalgar. To the mutineers those battles, and especially Trafalgar, were a plenary absolution, and a grand one; for that which goes to make up scenic naval display is heroic magnificence in arms. Those battles, especially Trafalgar, stand unmatched in human annals.

IV

Concerning "The greatest sailor since the world began."—
                                                    Tennyson.

In this matter of writing, resolve as one may to keep
to the main road, some by-paths have an enticement not
readily to be withstood. Beckoned by the genius of Nelson
I am going to err into such a by-path. If the reader will
keep me company I shall be glad. At the least we can
promise ourselves that pleasure which is wickedly said to
be in sinning, for a literary sin the divergence will be.

Very likely it is no new remark that the inventions of
our time have at last brought about a change in sea warfare in degree corresponding to the revolution in all warfare effected by the original introduction from China into
Europe of gunpowder. The first European firearm, a
clumsy contrivance, was, as is well-known, scouted by no
few of the knights as a base implement, good enough peradventure for weavers too craven to stand up crossing steel
with steel in frank fight. But as ashore knightly valour,
though shorn of its blazonry, did not cease with the knights,
neither on the seas, though nowadays in encounters there
a certain kind of displayed gallantry be fallen out of date
as hardly applicable under changed circumstances, did the
nobler qualities of such naval magnates as Don John of
Austria, Doria, Van Tromp, Jean Bart, the long line of
British admirals and the American Decaturs of 1812 become obsolete with their wooden walls.

Nevertheless, to anybody who can hold the Present at
its worth without being inappreciative of the Past, it may
be forgiven, if to such an one the solitary old hulk at Portsmouth, Nelson's *Victory,* seems to float there, not alone
as the decaying monument of a fame incorruptible, but
also as a poetic reproach, softened by its picturesqueness,
to the *Monitors* and yet mightier hulls of the European
ironclads. And this not altogether because such craft are
unsightly, unavoidably lacking the symmetry and grand
lines of the old battle-ships, but equally for other reasons.

There are some, perhaps, who while not altogether in-
accessible to that poetic reproach just alluded to, may yet
on behalf of the new order be disposed to parry it; and
this to the extent of iconoclasm, if need be. For example,
prompted by the sight of the star inserted in the *Victory's*
deck designating the spot where the Great Sailor fell, these
martial utilitarians may suggest considerations implying
that Nelson's ornate publication of his person in battle was
not only unnecessary, but not military, nay, savoured of
foolhardiness and vanity. They may add, too, that at Trafalgar it was in effect nothing less than a challenge to
death; and death came; and that but for his bravado the
victorious admiral might possibly have survived the battle,
and so, instead of having his sagacious dying injunctions
overruled by his immediate successor in command, he himself when the contest was decided might have brought his
shattered fleet to anchor, a proceeding which might have
averted the deplorable loss of life by shipwreck in the elemental tempest that followed the martial one.

Well, should we set aside the more than disputable
point whether for various reasons it was possible to anchor
the fleet, then plausibly enough the Benthamites of war
may urge the above.

But he *might have been* is but boggy ground to build
on. And certainly in foresight as to the larger issue of an
encounter, and anxious preparations for it—buoying the
deadly way and mapping it out, as at Copenhagen—few
commanders have been so painstakingly circumspect as
this reckless declarer of his person in fight.

Personal prudence, even when dictated by quite other
than selfish considerations, is surely no special virtue in a
military man; while an excessive love of glory, exercising
to the uttermost the honest heart-felt sense of duty, is the
first. If the name *Wellington* is not so much of a trumpet
to the blood as the simpler name *Nelson,* the reason for
this may perhaps be inferred from the above. Alfred in his
funeral ode on the victor of Waterloo ventures not to call
him the greatest soldier of all time, though in the same ode
he invokes Nelson as "the greatest sailor since the world
began."

At Trafalgar Nelson, on the brink of opening the fight, sat down and wrote his last brief will and testament. If under the presentiment of the most magnificent of all victories, to be crowned by his own glorious death, a sort of priestly motive led him to dress his person in the jewelled vouchers of his own shining deeds; if thus to have adorned himself for the altar and the sacrifice were indeed vainglory, then affectation and fustian is each truly heroic line in the great epics and dramas, since in such lines the poet but embodies in verse those exaltations of sentiment that a nature like Nelson, the opportunity being given, vitalises into acts.

V

The outbreak at the Nore was put down. But not every grievance was redressed. If the contractors for example, were no longer permitted to ply some practices peculiar to their tribe everywhere, such as providing shoddy cloth, rations not sound, or false in the measure; not the less impressment, for one thing, went on. By custom sanctioned for centuries, and judicially maintained by a Lord Chancellor as late as Mansfield, that mode of manning the fleet, a mode now fallen into a sort of abeyance but never formally renounced, it was not practicable to give up in those years. Its abrogation would have crippled the indispensable fleet, one wholly under canvas, no steam-power, its innumerable sails and thousands of cannon, everything in short, worked by muscle alone; a fleet the more insatiate in demand for men, because then multiplying its ships of all grades against contingencies present and to come of the convulsed Continent.

Discontent foreran the Two Mutinies, and more or less it lurkingly survived them. Hence it was not unreasonable to apprehend some return of trouble sporadic or general. One instance of such apprehensions: In the same year with this story, Nelson, then Vice-Admiral Sir Horatio, being with the fleet off the Spanish coast, was directed by the admiral in command to shift his pennant from the *Captain* to the *Theseus;* and for this reason: that the latter ship having newly arrived in the station from home where it had taken part in the Great Mutiny, danger was apprehended from the temper of the men; and it was thought that an officer like Nelson was the one, not indeed to terrorise the crew into base subjection, but to win them by force of his mere presence back to an allegiance, if not as enthusiastic as his own, yet as true. So it was, that for a time on more than one quarter-deck anxiety did exist. At sea precautionary vigilance was strained against relapse. At short notice an engagement might come on. When it did, the lieutenants assigned to batteries felt it incumbent on them in some instances to stand with drawn swords behind the men working the guns.

But on board the seventy-four in which Billy now swung his hammock very little in the manner of the men and nothing obvious in the demeanour of the officers would have suggested to an ordinary observer that the Great Mutiny was a recent event. In their general bearing and conduct the commissioned officers of a warship naturally take their tone from the commander, that is if he have that ascendancy of character that ought to be his.

Captain the Honourable Edward Fairfax Vere, to give him his full title, was a bachelor of forty or thereabouts, a sailor of distinction, even in a time prolific of renowned seamen. Though allied to the higher nobility, his advancement had not been altogether owing to influences connected with that circumstance. He had seen much service, been in various engagements, always acquitting himself as an officer mindful of the welfare of his men, but never tolerating an infraction of discipline; thoroughly versed in the science of his profession, and intrepid to the verge of temerity, though never injudiciously so. For his gallantry in the West Indian waters as flag-lieutenant under Rodney in that admiral's crowning victory over de Grasse, he was made a post-captain.

Ashore in the garb of a civilian, scarce anyone would have taken him for a sailor, more especially that he never garnished unprofessional talk with nautical terms, and grave in his bearing, evinced little appreciation of mere humour. It was not out of keeping with these traits that on a passage when nothing demanded his paramount action, he was the most undemonstrative of men. Any landsman observing this gentleman, not conspicuous by his stature and wearing no pronounced insignia, emerging from his retreat to the open deck, and noting the silent deference of the officers retiring to leeward, might have taken him for the King's guest, a civilian aboard the King's ship, some highly honourable discreet envoy on his way to an important post. But, in fact, this unobtrusiveness of demeanour may have proceeded from a certain unaffected modesty of manhood sometimes accompanying a resolute nature, a modesty evinced at all times not calling for pronounced action, and which shown in any rank of life suggests a virtue aristocratic in kind.

As with some others engaged in various departments of the world's more heroic activities, Captain Vere, though practical enough upon occasion, would at times betray a certain dreaminess of mood. Standing alone on the weather-side of the greater deck, one hand holding by the rigging, he would absently gaze off at the black sea. At the presentation to him of some minor matter interrupting the current of his thoughts, he would show more or less irascibility; but instantly he would control it.

In the Navy he was popularly known by the appellation —Starry Vere. How such a designation happened to fall upon one who, whatever his sturdy qualities, was without any brilliant ones, was in this wise: a favourite kinsman, Lord Denton, a freehanded fellow, had been the first to meet and congratulate him upon his return to England from the West Indian cruise; and but the day previous turning over a copy of Andrew Marvell's poems had lighted, not for the first time however, upon the lines entitled "Appleton House," the name of one of the seats of their common ancestor, a hero in the German wars of the seventeenth century, in which poem occur the lines,

> "This 'tis to have been from the first
> In a domestic heaven nursed,
> Under the discipline severe
> Of Fairfax and the starry Vere."

And so, upon embracing his cousin fresh from Rodney's victory, wherein he had played so gallant a part, brimming over with just family pride in the sailor of their house, he exuberantly exclaimed, "Give ye joy, Ed; give ye joy, my starry Vere!" This got currency, and the novel prefix serving in familiar parlance readily to distinguish the *Indomitable's* captain from another Vere, his senior, a distant relative, an officer of like rank in the Navy, it remained permanently attached to the surname.

VI

In view of the part that the commander of the *Indomitable* plays in scenes shortly to follow, it may be well to fill out that sketch of him outlined in the previous chapter. Aside from his qualities as a sea-officer Captain Vere was an exceptional character. Unlike no few of England's renowned sailors, long and arduous service with signal devotion to it had not resulted in absorbing and *salting* the entire man. He had a marked leaning toward everything intellectual. He loved books, never going to sea without a newly replenished library, compact but of the best. The isolated leisure, in some cases so wearisome, falling at intervals to commanders even during a war-cruise, never was tedious to Captain Vere. With nothing of that literary taste which less heeds the thing conveyed than the vehicle, his bias was toward those books to which every serious mind of superior order, occupying any active post of authority in the world, naturally inclines; books treating of actual men and events, no matter of what era—history, biography, and unconventional writers who, free from cant and convention, like Montaigne, honestly, and in the spirit of common sense, philosophise upon realities.

In this love of reading he found confirmation of his own more reserved thoughts—confirmation which he had vainly sought in social converse, so that as touching most fundamental topics, there had got to be established in him some positive convictions which he felt would abide in him essentially unmodified so long as his intelligent part remained unimpaired. In view of the humbled period in which his lot was cast, this was well for him. His settled convictions were as a dyke against those invading waters of novel opinion, social, political, and otherwise, which carried away as in a torrent no few minds in those days, minds by nature not inferior to his own. While other members of that aristocracy to which by birth he belonged were incensed at the innovators mainly because their theories were inimical to the privileged classes, Captain Vere disinterestedly opposed them not alone because they seemed to him incapable of embodiment in lasting institutions, but at war with the world and the peace of mankind.

With minds less stored than his and less earnest, some officers of his rank, with whom at times he would necessarily consort, found him lacking in the companionable quality, a dry and bookish gentleman as they deemed. Upon any chance withdrawal from their company one would be apt to say to another something like this! "Vere is a noble fellow, 'Starry Vere.' 'Spite the Gazettes Sir Horatio is at bottom scarce a better seaman or fighter. But between you and me now, don't you think there is a queer streak of the pedantic running through him? Yes, like the King's yarn in a coil of navy-rope."

Some apparent ground there was for this sort of confidential criticism, since not only did the captain's discourse never fall into the jocosely familiar, but in illustrating any point touching the stirring personages and events of the time, he would cite some historical character or incident of antiquity with the same easy air that he would cite from the moderns. He seemed unmindful of the circumstance that to his bluff company such allusions, however pertinent they might really be, were altogether alien to men whose reading was mainly confined to the journals. But considerateness in such matters is not easy in natures constituted like Captain Vere's. Their honesty prescribes to them directness, sometimes far-reaching like that of a migratory fowl that in its flight never heeds when it crosses a frontier.

VII

The lieutenants and other commissioned gentlemen forming Captain Vere's staff it is not necessary here to particularise, nor needs it to make mention of any of the warrant-officers. But among the petty officers was one who, having much to do with the story, may as well be forthwith introduced. This portrait I essay, but shall never hit it.

This was John Claggart, the master-at-arms. But that sea-title may to landsmen seem somewhat equivocal. Originally, doubtless, that petty officer's function was the instruction of the men in the use of arms, sword, or cutlass. But very long ago, owing to the advance in gunnery, making hand-to-hand encounters less frequent, and giving to nitre and sulphur the pre-eminence over steel, that function ceased; the master-at-arms of a great warship becoming a sort of chief of police charged among other matters with the duty of preserving order on the populous lower gun-decks.

Claggart was a man of about five-and-thirty, somewhat spare and tall, yet of no ill figure upon the whole. His hand was too small and shapely to have been accustomed to hard toil. The face was a notable one; the features, all except the chin, cleanly cut as those on a Greek medallion; yet the chin, beardless as Tecumseh's, had something of the strange protuberant heaviness in its make that recalled the prints of the Rev. Dr. Titus Oates, the historical deponent with the clerical drawl in the time of Charles II, and the fraud of the alleged Popish Plot. It served Claggart in his office that his eye could cast a tutoring glance. His brow was of the sort phrenologically associated with more than average intellect; silken jet curls, partly clustering over it, making a foil to the pallor below, a pallor tinged with a faint shade of amber akin to the hue of time-tinted marbles of old.

This complexion singularly contrasting with the red or deeply bronzed visages of the sailors, and in part the result of his official seclusion from the sunlight, though it *he doesn't quite fit the sailor stereotype.*

something wrong in physical being

was not exactly displeasing, nevertheless seemed to hint of something defective or abnormal in the constitution and blood. But his general aspect and manner were so suggestive of an education and career incongruous with his naval function, that when not actively engaged in it he looked like a man of high quality, social and moral, who for reasons of his own was keeping incognito. Nothing was known of his former life. It might be that he was an Englishman; and yet there lurked a bit of accent in his speech suggesting that possibly he was not such by birth, but through naturalisation in early childhood. Among certain grizzled sea-gossips of the gun-decks and forecastle went a rumour perdue that the master-at-arms was a chevalier who had volunteered into the King's Navy by way of compounding for some mysterious swindle whereof he had been arraigned at the King's Bench. The fact that nobody could substantiate this report was, of course, nothing against its secret currency. Such a rumour once started on the gun-decks in reference to almost anyone below the rank of a commissioned officer would, during the period assigned to this narrative, have seemed not altogether wanting in credibility to the tarry old wiseacres of a man-of-war crew. And indeed a man of Claggart's accomplishments, without prior nautical experience entering the Navy at mature life, as he did, and necessarily allotted at the start to the lowest grade in it; a man, too, who never made allusion to his previous life ashore; these were circumstances which in the dearth of exact knowledge as to his true antecedents opened to the invidious a vague field for unfavourable surmise.

But the sailors' dog-watch gossip concerning him derived a vague plausibility from the fact that now for some period the British Navy could so little afford to be squeamish in the matter of keeping up the muster-rolls, that not only were press-gangs notoriously abroad both afloat and ashore, but there was little or no secret about another matter, namely, that the London police were at liberty to capture any able-bodied suspect, and any questionable fellow at large, and summarily ship him to the dock-yard or fleet. Furthermore, even among voluntary enlistments, there were instances where the motive thereto partook neither of patriotic impulse not yet of a random desire to experience a bit of sea-life and martial adventure. Insolvent debtors of minor grade, together with the promiscuous lame ducks of morality, found in the Navy a convenient and secure refuge. Secure, because once enlisted aboard a King's ship, they were as much in sanctuary as the transgressor of the Middle Ages harbouring himself under the shadow of the altar. Such sanctioned irregularities, which for obvious reasons the Government would hardly think to parade at the time, and which consequently, and as affecting the least influential class of mankind, have all but dropped into oblivion, lend colour to something for the truth whereof I do not vouch, and hence have some scruple in stating; something I remember having seen in print, though the book I cannot recall; but the same thing was personally communicated to me now more than forty years ago by an old pensioner in a cocked hat, with whom I had a most interesting talk on the terrace at Greenwich, a Baltimore negro, a Trafalgar man. It was to this effect: In the case of a warship short of hands, whose speedy sailing was imperative, the deficient quota, in lack of any other way of making it good, would be eked out by drafts called direct from the jails. For reasons previously suggested it would not perhaps be easy at the present day directly to prove or disprove the allegation. But allowed as a verity, how significant would it be of England's straits at the time, confronted by these wars which like a flight of harpies rose shrieking from the din and dust of the fallen Bastille. That era appears measurably clear to us who look back at it, and but read of it. But to the grandfathers of us greybeards, the thoughtful of them, the genius of it presented an aspect like that of Camoens' "Spirit of the Cape," an eclipsing menace mysterious and prodigious. Not America was exempt from apprehension. At the height of Napoleon's unexampled conquests, there were Americans who had fought at Bunker Hill who looked forward to the possibility that the Atlantic might prove no barrier against the ultimate schemes of this portentous upstart from the revolutionary chaos, who seemed in act of fulfilling judgment prefigured in the Apocalypse.

But the less credence was to be given to the gun-deck talk touching Claggart, seeing that no man holding his office in a man-of-war can ever hope to be popular with the crew. Besides, in derogatory comments upon one against whom they have a grudge, or for any reason mislike, sailors are much like landsmen, they are apt to exaggerate or romance.

About as much was really known to the *Indomitable's* tars of the master-at-arms' career before entering the service as an astronomer knows about a comet's travels prior to its first observable appearance in the sky. The verdict of the sea-quidnuncs has been cited only by way of showing what sort of moral impression the man made upon rude uncultivated natures, whose conceptions of human wickedness were necessarily of the narrowest, limited to ideas of vulgar rascality—a thief among the swinging hammocks during a night-watch, or the man-brokers and land-sharks of the seaports.

It was no gossip, however, but fact, that though, as before hinted, Claggart upon his entrance into the navy was, as a novice, assigned to the least honourable section of a man-of-war's crew, embracing the drudges, he did not long remain there.

The superior capacity he immediately evinced, his constitutional sobriety, ingratiating deference to superiors, together with a peculiar ferreting genius manifested on a singular occasion, all this capped by a certain austere patriotism, abruptly advanced him to the position of master-at-arms.

Of this maritime chief of police the ship's corporals, so called, were the immediate subordinates, and compliant ones; and this, as is to be noted in some business departments ashore, almost to a degree inconsistent with entire moral volition. His place put various converging wires of underground influence under the chief's control, capable when astutely worked through his under-strappers of operating to the mysterious discomfort, if nothing worse, of any of the sea-commonalty.

VIII

Life in the foretop well agreed with Billy Budd. There, when not actually engaged on the yards yet higher aloft, the topmen, who as such had been picked out for youth and activity, constituted an aerial club, lounging at ease against the smaller stun'-sails rolled up into cushions, spinning yarns like the lazy gods, and frequently amused with what was going on in the busy world of the decks below. No wonder then that a young fellow of Billy's disposition was well content in such society. Giving no cause of offence to anybody, he was always alert at a call. So in the merchant service it had been with him. But now such punctiliousness in duty was shown that his topmates would sometimes good-naturedly laugh at him for it. This heightened alacrity had its cause, namely: the impression made upon him by the first formal gangway-punishment he had ever witnessed, which befell the day following his impressment. It had been incurred by a little fellow, young, a novice, an after-guardsman absent from his assigned post when the ship was being put about, a dereliction resulting in a rather serious hitch to that manœuvre, one demanding instantaneous promptitude in letting go and making fast. When Billy saw the culprit's naked back under the scourge gridironed with red welts, and worse; when he marked the dire expression in the liberated man's face, as with his woollen shirt flung over him by the executioner he rushed forward from the spot to bury himself in the crowd, Billy was horrified. He resolved that never through remissness would he make himself liable to such a visitation, or do or omit aught that might merit even verbal reproof. What then was his surprise and concern when ultimately he found himself getting into petty trouble occasionally about such matters as the stowage of his bag, or something amiss in his hammock, matters under the police oversight of the ship's corporals of the lower decks, and which brought down on him a vague threat from one of them.

So heedful in all things as he was, how could this be? He could not understand it, and it more than vexed him.

When he spoke to his young topmates about it, they were either lightly incredulous, or found something comical in his unconcealed anxiety. "Is it your bag, Billy?" said one; "well, sew yourself up in it, Billy boy, and then you'll be sure to know if anybody meddles with it."

Now there was a veteran aboard who, because his years began to disqualify him from more active work, had been recently assigned duty as mainmast-man in his watch, looking to the gear belayed at the rail round about that great spar near the deck. At off-times the foretopman had picked up some acquaintance with him, and now in his trouble it occurred to him that he might be the sort of person to go for wise counsel. He was an old Dansker long anglicised in the service, of few words, many wrinkles and some honourable scars. His wizened face, time-tinted and weather-stormed to the complexion of an antique parchment, was here and there peppered blue by the chance explosion of a gun-carriage in action. He was an *Agamemnon* man; some two years prior to the time of this story having served under Nelson, when but Sir Horatio, in that ship immortal in naval memory, and which, dismantled and in parts broken up to her bare ribs, is seen a grand skeleton in Haydon's etching. As one of a boarding-party from the *Agamemnon* he had received a cut slantwise along one temple and cheek, leaving a long pale scar like a streak of dawn's light falling athwart the dark visage. It was on account of that scar and the affair in which it was known that he had received it, as well as from his blue-peppered complexion, that the Dansker went among the *Indomitable's* crew by the name of "Board-her-in-the-smoke."

Now the first time that his small weasel eyes happened to light on Billy Budd, a certain grim internal merriment set all his ancient wrinkles into antic play. Was it that his eccentric unsentimental old sapience, primitive in its kind, saw, or thought it saw, something which in contrast with the warship's environment looked oddly incongruous in the Handsome Sailor? But after slyly studying him at intervals, the old Merlin's equivocal merriment was modified by now. For now when the twain would meet, it would start in his face a quizzing sort of look, but it would be but momentary and sometimes replaced by an expression of speculative query as to what might eventually befall a nature like that, dropped into a world not without some mantraps and against whose subtleties simple courage lacking experience and address and without any touch of defensive ugliness, is of little avail; and where such innocence as man is capable of does yet in a moral emergency not always sharpen the faculties or enlighten the will.

However it was, the Dansker in his ascetic way rather took to Billy. Nor was this only because of a certain philosophic interest in such a character. There was another cause. While the old man's eccentricities, sometimes bordering on the ursine, repelled the juniors, Billy, undeterred thereby, would make advances, never passing the old *Agamemnon* man without a salutation marked by that respect which is seldom lost on the aged, however crabbed at times, or whatever their station in life. There was a vein of dry humour, or what not, in the mastman; and whether in freak of patriarchal irony touching Billy's youth and athletic frame, or for some other and more recondite reason, from the first in addressing him he always substituted Baby for Billy. The Dansker, in fact, being the originator of the name by which the foretopman eventually became known aboard ship.

Well then, in his mysterious little difficulty going in quest of the wrinkled one, Billy found him off duty in a dogwatch ruminating by himself, seated on a shot-box of the upper gun-deck, now and then surveying with a somewhat cynical regard certain of the more swaggering promenaders there. Billy recounted his trouble, again wondering how it all happened. The salt seer attentively listened, accompanying the foretopman's recitals with queer twitchings of his wrinkles and problematical little sparkles of his small ferret eyes. Making an end of his story, the foretopman asked, "And now, Dansker, do tell me what you think of it." The old man, shoving up the front of his tarpaulin and deliberately rubbing the long slant scar at the point where it entered the thin hair, laconically said, "Baby Budd, *Jemmy Legs*" (meaning the master-at-arms) "is down on you."

"Jemmy Legs!" ejaculated Billy, his welkin eyes expanding; "what for? Why, he calls me *the sweet and pleasant young fellow,* they tell me."

"Does he so?" grinned the grizzled one; then said, "Ay, Baby lad, a sweet voice has *Jemmy Legs.*"

"No, not always. But to me he has. I seldom pass him but there comes a pleasant word."

"And that's because he's down upon you, Baby Budd."

Such reiteration, along with the manner of it, incomprehensible to a novice, disturbed Billy almost as much as the mystery for which he had sought explanation. Something less unpleasingly oracular he tried to extract; but the old sea-Chiron, thinking perhaps that for the nonce he had sufficiently instructed his young Achilles, pursed his lips, gathered all his wrinkles together, and would commit himself to nothing further.

Years, and those experiences which befall certain shrewder men subordinated life-long to the will of superiors, all this had developed in the Dansker the pithy guarded cynicism that was his leading characteristic.

IX

The next day an incident served to confirm Billy Budd in his incredulity as to the Dansker's strange summing-up of the case submitted.

The ship at noon going large before the wind was rolling on her course, and he, below at dinner and engaged in some sportful talk with the members of his mess, chanced in a sudden lurch to spill the entire contents of his soup-pan upon the new-scrubbed deck. Claggart, the master-at-arms, official rattan in hand, happened to be passing along the battery in a bay of which the mess was lodged, and the greasy liquid streamed just across his path. Stepping over it, he was proceeding on his way without comment, since the matter was nothing to take notice of under the circumstances, when he happened to observe who it was that had done the spilling. His countenance changed. Pausing, he was about to ejaculate something hasty at the sailor, but checked himself, and pointing down to the streaming soup, playfully tapped him from behind with his rattan, saying, in a low musical voice, peculiar to him at times, "Handsomely done, my lad! And handsome is as handsome did it, too!" and with that passed on. Not noted by Billy as not coming within his view was the involuntary smile, or rather grimace, that accompanied Claggart's equivocal words. Aridly he drew down the thin corners of his shapely mouth. But everybody taking his remark as meant for humorous, and at which therefore as coming from a superior they were bound to laugh, "with counterfeited glee," acted accordingly; and Billy, tickled, it may be, by the allusion to his being the Handsome Sailor, merrily joined in; then addressing his messmates exclaimed, "There, now, who says that Jemmy Legs is down on me!"

"And who said he was, Beauty?" demanded one Donald with some surprise. Whereat the foretopman looked a little foolish, recalling that it was only one person, Board-her-in-the-smoke, who had suggested what to him was the smoky idea that this pleasant master-at-arms was in any peculiar way hostile to him. Meantime that functionary resuming his path must have momentarily worn some expression less guarded than that of the bitter smile and, usurping the face from the heart, some distorting expression perhaps, for a drummer-boy, heedlessly frolicking along from the opposite direction, and chancing to come into light collision with his person, was strangely disconcerted by his aspect. Nor was the impression lessened when the official, impulsively giving him a sharp cut with the rattan, vehemently exclaimed, "Look where you go!"

X

What was the matter with the master-at-arms? And be the matter what it might, how could it have direct relation to Billy Budd, with whom prior to the affair of the spilled soup he had never come into any special contact, official or otherwise? What indeed could the trouble have to do with one so little inclined to give offence as the merchant ship's *peacemaker,* even him who in Claggart's own phrase was "the sweet and pleasant young fellow"? Yes, why should *Jemmy Legs,* to borrow the Dansker's expression, be *down* on the Handsome Sailor?

But, at heart and not for nothing, as the late chance encounter may indicate to the discerning, down on him, secretly down on him, he assuredly was.

Now to invent something touching the more private career of Claggart, something involving Billy Budd, of which something the latter should be wholly ignorant, some romantic incident implying that Claggart's knowledge of the young blue-jacket began at some period anterior to catching sight of him on board the seventy-four—all this, not so difficult to do, might avail in a way more or less interesting to account for whatever enigma may appear to lurk in the case. But, in fact, there was nothing of the sort. And yet the cause, necessarily to be assumed as the sole one assignable, is in its very realism as much charged with that prime element of Radcliffian romance, *the mysterious,* as any that the ingenuity of the author of the *Mysteries of Udolpho* could devise. For what can more partake of the mysterious than an antipathy spontaneous and profound such as is evoked in certain exceptional mortals by the mere aspect of some other mortal, however harmless he may be?—if not called forth by that very harmlessness itself.

Now there can exist no irritating juxtaposition of dissimilar personalities comparable to that which is possible aboard a great warship fully manned and at sea. There, every day, among all ranks, almost every man comes into more or less of contact with almost every other man. Wholly there to avoid even the sight of an aggravating object one must needs give it Jonah's toss, or jump overboard himself. Imagine how all this might eventually operate on some peculiar human creature the direct reverse of a saint?

But for the adequate comprehending of Claggart by a normal nature these hints are insufficient. To pass from a normal nature to him one must cross "the deadly space between," and this is best done by indirection.

Long ago an honest scholar, my senior, said to me in reference to one who like himself is now no more, a man so unimpeachably respectable that against him nothing was ever openly said, though among the few something was whispered, "Yes, X——is a nut not to be cracked by the tap of a lady's fan. You are aware that I am the adherent of no organised religion, much less of any philosophy built into a system. Well, for all that, I think that to try and get into X——, enter his labyrinth, and get out again, without a clue derived from some source other than what is known as *knowledge of the world,* that were hardly possible, at least for me."

"Why," said I, "X——, however singular a study to some, is yet human, and knowledge of the world assuredly implies the knowledge of human nature, and in most of its varieties."

"Yes, but a superficial knowledge of it, serving ordinary purposes. But for anything deeper I am not certain whether to know the world and to know human nature be not two distinct branches of knowledge, which while they may coexist in the same heart, yet either may exist with little or nothing of the other. Nay, in an average man of the world, his constant rubbing with it blunts that fine spiritual insight indispensable to the understanding of the essential in certain exceptional characters, whether evil ones or good. In a matter of some importance I have seen a girl wind an old lawyer about her little finger. Nor was it dotage of senile love. Nothing of the sort. But he knew law better than he knew the girl's heart. Coke and Blackstone hardly shed so much light into obscure spiritual places as the Hebrew prophets. And who were they? Mostly recluses."

At the time my inexperience was such that I did not quite see the drift of all this. It may be that I see it now. And, indeed, if that lexicon which is based on Holy Writ were any longer popular, one might with less difficulty define and denominate certain phenomenal men. As it is, one must turn to some authority not liable to the charge of being tinctured with the Biblical element.

In a list of definitions included in the authentic trans-

claggart wanted to like Billy but could not because of his...

lation of Plato, a list is attributed to him, occurs this: "Natural Depravity: a depravity according to nature." A definition which, though savouring of Calvinism, by no means involves Calvin's dogma as to total mankind. Evidently its intent makes it applicable but to individuals. Not many are the examples of this depravity which the gallows and jail supply. At any rate, for notable instances—since these have no vulgar alloy of the brute in them, but invariably are dominated by intellectuality—one must go elsewhere. Civilisation, especially if of the austerer sort, is auspicious to it. It folds itself in the mantle of respectability. It has its certain negative virtues serving as silent auxiliaries. It is not going too far to say that it is without vices or small sins. There is a phenomenal pride in it that excludes them from anything—never mercenary or avaricious. In short, the depravity here meant partakes nothing of the sordid or sensual. It is serious, but free from acerbity. Though no flatterer of mankind, it never speaks ill of it.

But the thing which in eminent instances signalises so exceptional a nature is this: though the man's even temper and discreet bearing would seem to intimate a mind peculiarly subject to the law of reason, not the less in his soul's recesses he would seem to riot in complete exemption from that law, having apparently little to do with reason further than to employ it as an ambidexter implement for effecting the irrational. That is to say: toward the accomplishment of an aim which is wantonness of malignity would seem to partake of the insane, he will direct a cool judgment sagacious and sound.

These men are true madmen, and of the most dangerous sort, for their lunacy is not continuous, but occasional; evoked by some special object; it is secretive and self-contained, so that when most active it is to the average mind not distinguished from sanity, and for the reason above suggested that whatever its aim may be, and the aim is never disclosed, the method and the outward proceeding is always perfectly rational.

Now something such was Claggart, in whom was the mania of an evil nature, not engendered by vicious training *was evoked by Billy.*

or corrupting books or licentious living, but born with him and innate, in short, "a depravity according to nature."

Can it be this phenomenon, disowned or not acknowledged, that in some criminal cases puzzles the courts? For this cause have our juries at times not only to endure the prolonged contentions of lawyers with their fees, but also the yet more perplexing strife of the medical experts with theirs? But why leave it to them? Why not subpoena as well the clerical proficients? Their vocation bringing them into peculiar contact with so many human beings, and sometimes in their least guarded hour, in interviews very much more confidential than those of physician and patient; this would seem to qualify them to know something about those intricacies involved in the question of moral responsibility; whether in a given case, say, the crime proceeded from mania in the brain or rabies of the heart. As to any differences among themselves these clerical proficients might develop on the stand, these could hardly be greater than the direct contradictions exchanged between the remunerated medical experts.

Dark sayings are these, some will say. But why? It is because they somewhat savour of Holy Writ in its phrase "mysteries of iniquity."

The point of the story turning on the hidden nature of the master-at-arms has necessitated this chapter. With an added hint or two in connection with the accident of the mess, the resumed narrative must be left to vindicate as it may its own credibility.

XI

PALE IRE, ENVY AND DESPAIR.

That Claggart's figure was not amiss, and his face, save the chin, well moulded, has already been said. Of these favourable points he seemed not insensible, for he was not only neat but careful in his dress. But the form of Billy Budd was heroic; and if his face was without the intellectual look of the pallid Claggart's, not the less was it lit, like his, from within, though from a different source. The bonfire in his heart made luminous the rose-tan in his cheek.

In view of the marked contrast between the persons of the twain, it is more than probable that when the master-at-arms in the scene last given applied to the sailor the proverb *"Handsome is as handsome does,"* he there let escape an ironic inkling, not caught by the young sailors who heard it, as to what it was that had first moved him against Billy, namely, his significant personal beauty.

Now envy and antipathy, passions irreconcilable in reason, nevertheless in fact may spring conjoined like Chang and Eng in one birth. Is envy then such a monster? Well, though many an arraigned mortal has in hopes of mitigated penalty pleaded guilty to horrible actions, did ever anybody seriously confess to envy? Something there is in it universally felt to be more shameful than even felonious crime. And not only does everybody disown it, but the better sort are inclined to incredulity when it is in earnest imputed to an intelligent man. But since its lodgment is in the heart, not the brain, no degree of intellect supplies a guarantee against it. But Claggart's was no vulgar form of the passion. Nor, as directed toward Billy Budd, did it partake of that streak of apprehensive jealousy that marred Saul's visage perturbedly brooding on the comely young David. Claggart's envy struck deeper. If askance he eyed the good looks, cheery health, and frank enjoyment of young life in Billy Budd, it was because these happened to go along with a nature that, as Claggart magnetically felt, had in its simplicity never willed malice, or experienced the reactionary bite of that serpent. To him, the spirit lodged within Billy and looking out from his welkin eyes as from windows, that ineffability which made the dimple in his dyed cheek, suppled his joints, and danced in his yellow curls, made him pre-eminently the Handsome Sailor. One person excepted, the master-at-arms was perhaps the only man in the ship intellectually capable of adequately appreciating the moral phenomenon presented which assuming various secret forms within him, at times in Billy Budd, and the insight but intensified his passion, assumed that of cynic disdain—disdain of innocence. To be nothing

Claggarts Natural Envy (depravity)

more than innocent! Yet in an aesthetic way he saw the charm of it, the courageous free-and-easy temper of it, and fain would have shared it, but he despaired of it.

With no power to annul the elemental evil in himself, though he could hide it readily enough; apprehending the good, but powerless to be it; what recourse is left to a nature like Claggart's, surcharged with energy as such natures almost invariably are, but to recoil upon itself, and, like the scorpion for which the Creator alone is responsible, act out to the end its allotted part?

Passion, and passion in its profoundest, is not a thing demanding a palatial stage whereon to play its part. Down among the groundlings, among the beggars and rakers of the garbage, profound passion is enacted. And the circumstances that provoke it, however trivial or mean, are no measure of its power. In the present instance the stage is a scrubbed gun-deck, and one of the external provocations a man-of-war's man's spilled soup.

Now when the master-at-arms noticed whence came that greasy fluid streaming before his feet, he must have taken it—to some extent wilfully perhaps—not for the mere accident it assuredly was, but for the sly escape of a spontaneous feeling on Billy's part more or less answering to the antipathy on his own. In effect a foolish demonstration he must have thought, and very harmless, like the futile kick of a heifer, which yet, were the heifer a shod stallion, would not be so harmless. Even so was it that into the gall of envy Claggart infused the vitriol of his contempt. But the incident confirmed to him certain tell-tale reports purveyed to his ear by *Squeak*, one of his more cunning corporals, a grizzled little man, so nicknamed by the sailors on account of his squeaky voice and sharp visage ferreting about the dark corners of the lower decks after interlopers, satirically suggesting to them the idea of a rat in a cellar.

Now his chief's employing him as an implicit tool in laying little traps for the worriment of the foretopman—for it was from the master-at-arms that the petty persecutions heretofore adverted to had proceeded—the corporal, having naturally enough concluded that his master could have no love for the sailor, made it his business, faithful understrapper that he was, to ferment the ill blood by perverting to his chief certain innocent frolics of the good-natured foretopman, besides inventing for his mouth sundry contumelious epithets he claimed to have overheard him let fall. The master-at-arms never suspected the <u>veracity</u> of these reports, more especially as to the epithets, for he well knew how secretly unpopular may become a master-at-arms—at least, a master-at-arms in those days, zealous in his function—and how the blue-jackets shoot at him in private their raillery and wit; the nickname by which he goes among them (*Jemmy Legs*) implying under the form of merriment their cherished disrespect and dislike.

In view of the greediness of hate for provocation, it hardly needed a purveyor to feed Claggart's passion. An uncommon prudence is habitual with the subtler depravity, for it has everything to hide. And in case of any merely suspected injury, its secretiveness voluntarily cuts it off from enlightenment or disillusion; and not unreluctantly, action is taken upon surmise as upon certainty. And the retaliation is apt to be in monstrous disproportion to the supposed offence; for when in anybody was revenge in its exactions aught else but an inordinate usurer? But how with Claggart's conscience? For though consciences are unlike as foreheads, every intelligence, not excluding the Scriptural devils who "believe and tremble," has one. But Claggart's conscience, being but the lawyer to his will, made ogres of trifles, probably arguing that the motive imputed to Billy in spilling the soup just when he did, together with the epithets alleged, these, if nothing more, made a strong case against him; nay, justified animosity into a sort of retributive righteousness. The Pharisee is the Guy Fawkes prowling in the hid chambers underlying some natures like Claggart's. And they can really form no conception of an unreciprocated malice. Probably, the master-at-arms' clandestine persecution of Billy was started to try the temper of the man; but it had not developed any quality in him that enmity could make official use of, or ever pervert into even plausible self-justification; so that the occurrence at the

mess, petty if it were, was a welcome one to that peculiar
conscience assigned to be the private mentor of Claggart;
and for the rest, not improbably, it put him upon new
experiments.

XII

Not many days after the last incident narrated, something befell Billy Budd that more gravelled him than aught
that had previously occurred.

It was a warm night for the latitude; and the foretopman, whose watch at the time was properly below, was
dozing on the uppermost deck whither he had ascended
from his hot hammock—one of hundreds suspended so
closely wedged together over a lower gun-deck that there
was little or no swing to them. He lay as in the shadow of
a hillside stretched under the lee of the *booms,* a piled
ridge of spare spars, and among which the ship's largest
boat, the launch, was stowed. Alongside of three other
slumberers from below, he lay near one end of the booms
which approached from the foremast; his station aloft on
duty as a foretopman being just over the deck station of
the forecastleman, entitling him according to usage to make
himself more or less at home in that neighbourhood.

Presently he was stirred into semi-consciousness by
somebody, who must have previously sounded the sleep
of the others, touching his shoulder, and then, as the foretopman raised his head, breathing into his ear in a quick
whisper, "Slip into the lee fore-chains, Billy; there is
something in the wind. Don't speak. Quick. I will meet you
there"; and who then disappeared.

Now Billy, like sundry other essentially good-natured
ones, had some of the weaknesses inseparable from essential good nature; and among these was a reluctance,
almost an incapacity, of plumply saying *no* to an abrupt
proposition not obviously absurd on the face of it, nor
obviously unfriendly, nor iniquitous. And being of warm
blood he had not the phlegm to negate any proposition
by unresponsive inaction. Like his sense of fear, his ap-

prehension as to aught outside of the honest and natural was seldom very quick. Besides, upon the present occasion, the drowse from his sleep still hung upon him.

However it was, he mechanically rose, and sleepily wondering what could be *in the wind,* betook himself to the designated place, a narrow platform, one of six, outside of the high bulwarks, and screened by the great deadeyes and multiple columned lanyards of the shrouds and back-stays; and, in a great warship of that time, of dimensions commensurate to the ample hull's magnitude; a tarry balcony, in short, overhanging the sea, and so secluded that one mariner of the *Indomitable,* a nonconformist old tar of a serious turn, made it even in daytime his private oratory.

In this retired nook the stranger soon joined Billy Budd. There was no moon as yet; a haze obscured the starlight. He could not distinctly see the stranger's face. Yet from something in the outline and carriage, Billy took him to be, and correctly, one of the afterguard.

"Hist, Billy!" said the man, in the same quick, cautionary whisper as before; "you were impressed, weren't you? Well, so was I"; and he paused, as to mark the effect. But Billy, not knowing exactly what to make of this, said nothing. Then the other: "We are not the only impressed ones, Billy. There's a gang of us. Couldn't you—help—at a pinch?"

"What do you mean?" demanded Billy, here shaking off his drowse.

"Hist, hist!" the hurried whisper now growing husky: "see here," and the man held up two small objects faintly twinkling in the night light; "see, they are yours, Billy, if you'll only——"

But Billy broke in, and in his resentful eagerness to deliver himself, his vocal infirmity somewhat intruded. "D-D-Damme, I don't know what you are d-driving at, or what you mean, but you had better g-g-go where you belong!" For the moment the fellow, as confounded, did not stir; and Billy, springing to his feet, said, "If you d-don't start, I'll t-t-t-oss you back over the r-rail!" There was no mistaking this, and the mysterious emissary decamped, disappearing in the direction of the mainmast in the shadow of the booms.

"Hallo, what's the matter?" here came growling from a forecastleman awakened from his deck-doze by Billy's raised voice. And as the foretopman reappeared, and was recognised by him, "Ah, *Beauty,* is it you? Well, something must have been the matter, for you st-st-stuttered."

"Oh," rejoined Billy, now mastering the impediment; "I found an afterguardsman in our part of the ship here, and I bid him be off where he belongs."

"And is that all you did about it, foretopman?" gruffly demanded another, an irascible old fellow of brick-coloured visage and hair, and who was known to his associate forecastlemen as *Red Pepper.* "Such sneaks I should like to marry to the gunner's daughter!" by that expression meaning that he would like to subject them to disciplinary castigation over a gun.

However, Billy's rendering of the matter satisfactorily accounted to these inquirers for the brief commotion, since of all the sections of a ship's company the forecastlemen, veterans for the most part, and bigoted in their sea-prejudices, are the most jealous in resenting territorial encroachments, especially on the part of any of the afterguard, of whom they have but a sorry opinion, chiefly landsmen, never going aloft except to reef or furl the mainsail, and in no wise competent to handle a marlingspike or turn in a *dead-eye,* say.

XIII

This incident sorely puzzled Billy Budd. It was an entirely new experience; the first time in his life that he had ever been personally approached in underhand intriguing fashion. Prior to this encounter he had known nothing of the afterguardsman, the two men being stationed wide apart, one forward and aloft during his watch, the other on deck and aft.

What could it mean? And could they really be guineas, those two glittering objects the interloper had held up to his (Billy's) eyes? Where could the fellow get guineas? Why, even buttons, spare buttons, are not so plentiful at sea. The more he turned the matter over, the more he was nonplussed, and made uneasy and discomforted. In his disgustful recoil from an overture which though he but ill comprehended he instinctively knew must involve evil of some sort, Billy Budd was like a young horse fresh from the pasture suddenly inhaling a vile whiff from some chemical factory, and by repeated snortings trying to get it out of his nostrils and lungs. This frame of mind barred all desire of holding further parley with the fellow, even were it but for the purpose of gaining some enlightenment as to his design in approaching him. And yet he was not without natural curiosity to see how such a visitor in the dark would look in broad day.

He espied him the following afternoon in his first dog-watch below, one of the smokers on that forward part of the upper gun-deck allotted to the pipe. He recognised him by his general cut and build, more than by his round freckled face and glassy eyes of pale blue veiled with lashes all but white. And yet Billy was a bit uncertain whether indeed it were he—yonder chap about his own age, chatting and laughing in free-hearted way, leaning against a gun; a genial young fellow enough to look at, and something of a rattle-brain, to all appearance. Rather chubby, too, for a sailor, even an afterguardsman. In short, the last man in the world, one would think, to be overburthened with thoughts, especially those perilous thoughts that must needs belong to a conspirator in any serious project, or even to the underling of such a conspirator.

Although Billy was not aware of it, the fellow with a sidelong watchful glance had perceived Billy first, and then noting that Billy was looking at him, thereupon nodded a familiar sort of friendly recognition as to an old acquaintance, without interrupting the talk he was engaged in with the group of smokers. A day or two afterwards, chancing

Billy's starting to ask, "why he is worr[ied]" ove[r] evil

in the evening promenade on a gun-deck to pass Billy, he offered a flying word of good-fellowship, as it were, which by its unexpectedness, and equivocalness under the circumstances, so embarrassed Billy, that he knew not how to respond to it, and let it go unnoticed.

Billy was now left more at a loss than before. The ineffectual speculations into which he was led were so disturbingly alien to him, that he did his best to smother them. It never entered his mind that here was a matter which, from its extreme questionableness, it was his duty as a loyal blue-jacket to report in the proper quarter. And, probably, had such a step been suggested to him, he would have been deterred from taking it by the thought, one of novice-magnanimity, that it would savour overmuch of the dirty work of a tell-tale. He kept the thing to himself. Yet upon one occasion he could not forbear a little disburthening himself to the old Dansker, tempted thereto perhaps by the influence of a balmy night when the ship lay becalmed; the twain, silent for the most part, sitting together on deck, their heads propped against the bulwarks. But it was only a partial and anonymous account that Billy gave, the unfounded scruples above referred to preventing full disclosure to anybody. Upon hearing Billy's version, the sage Dansker seemed to divine more than he was told; and after a little meditation, during which his wrinkles were pursed as into a point, quite effacing for the time that quizzing expression his face sometimes wore—"Didn't I say so, Baby Budd?"

"Say what?" demanded Billy.

"Why, *Jemmy Legs* is *down* on you."

"And what," rejoined Billy in amazement, "has *Jemmy Legs* to do with that cracked afterguardsman?"

"Ho, it was an afterguardsman, then. A cat's-paw, a cat's-paw!" And with that exclamation, which, whether it had reference to a light puff of air just then coming over the calm sea, or subtler relation to the afterguardsman, there is no telling. The old Merlin gave a twisting wrench with his black teeth at his plug of tobacco, vouchsafing no reply to Billy's impetuous question. For it was his wont to relapse into grim silence when interrogated in sceptical sort as to any of his sententious oracles, not always very clear ones, rather partaking of that obscurity which invests most Delphic deliverances from any quarter.

XIV

Long experience had very likely brought this old man to that bitter prudence which never interferes in aught, and never gives advice.

Yet, despite the Dansker's pithy insistence as to the master-at-arms being at the bottom of these strange experiences of Billy on board the *Indomitable,* the young sailor was ready to ascribe them to almost anybody but the man who, to use Billy's own expression, "always had a pleasant word for him." This is to be wondered at. Yet not so much to be wondered at. In certain matters some sailors even in mature life remain unsophisticated enough. But a young seafarer of the disposition of our athletic foretopman is much of a child-man. And yet a child's utter innocence is but its blank ignorance, and the innocence more or less wanes as intelligence waxes. But in Billy Budd intelligence, such as it was, had advanced, while yet his simple-mindedness remained for the most part unaffected. Experience is a teacher indeed; yet did Billy's years make his experience small. Besides, he had none of that intuitive knowledge of the bad which in natures not good or incompletely so, fore-runs experience, and therefore may pertain, as in some instances it too clearly does pertain, even to youth.

And what could Billy know of man except of man as a mere sailor? And the old-fashioned sailor, the veritable man-before-the-mast, the sailor from boyhood up, he, though indeed of the same species as a landsman, is in some respects singularly distinct from him. The sailor is frankness, the landsman is finesse. Life is not a game with the sailor, demanding the long head; no intricate game of chess where few moves are made in straight-forwardness, but ends are attained by indirection; an oblique, tedious, barren game, hardly worth that poor candle burnt out in playing it.

chess board - using crew
as pawns -
against
Bil

Yes, as a class, sailors are in character a juvenile race. Even their deviations are marked by juvenility. And this more especially held true with the sailors of Billy's time. Then, too, certain things which apply to all sailors do more pointedly operate here and there upon the junior one. Every sailor, too, is accustomed to obey orders without debating them; his life afloat is externally ruled for him; he is not brought into that promiscuous commerce with mankind where unobstructed free agency on equal terms —equal superficially, at least—soon teaches one that unless upon occasion he exercises a distrust keen in proportion to the fairness of the appearance, some foul turn may be served him. A ruled, undemonstrative distrustfulness is so habitual, not with business-men so much, as with men who know their kind in less shallow relations than business, namely certain men of the world, that they come at last to employ it all but unconsciously; and some of them would very likely feel real surprise at being charged with it as one of their general characteristics.

XV

But after the little matter at the mess Billy Budd no more found himself in strange trouble at times about his hammock or his clothes-bag, or what not. While, as to that smile that occasionally sunned him, and the pleasant passing word, these were, if not more frequent, yet if anything more pronounced than before.

But for all that, there were certain other demonstrations now. When Claggart's unobserved glance happened to light on belted Billy rolling along the upper gun-deck in the leisure of the second dog-watch, exchanging passing broadsides of fun with other young promenaders in the crowd, that glance would follow the cheerful sea-Hyperion with a settled meditative and melancholy expression, his eyes strangely suffused with incipient feverish tears. Then would Claggart look like the man of sorrows. Yes, and sometimes the melancholy expression would have in it a touch of soft yearning, as if Claggart could even have loved Billy but for fate and ban. But this was an evanescence, and quickly repented of, as it were, by an immitigable look, pinching and shrivelling the visage into the momentary semblance of a wrinkled walnut. But sometimes catching sight in advance of the foretopman coming in his direction, he would, upon their nearing, step aside a little to let him pass, dwelling upon Billy for the moment with the glittering dental satire of a guise. But upon any abrupt unforeseen encounter a red light would flash forth from his eye, like a spark from an anvil in a dusk smithy. That quick fierce light was a strange one, darted from orbs which in repose were of a colour nearest approaching a deeper violet, the softest of shades.

Though some of these caprices of the pit could not but be observed by their object, yet were they beyond the construing of such a nature. And the thews of Billy were hardly comparable with that sort of sensitive spiritual organisation which in some cases instinctively conveys to ignorant innocence an admonition of the proximity of the malign. He thought the master-at-arms acted in a manner rather queer at times. That was all. But the occasional frank air and pleasant word went for what they purported to be, the young sailor never having heard as yet of the "too fair-spoken man."

Had the foretopman been conscious of having done or said anything to provoke the ill-will of the official, it would have been different with him, and his sight might have been purged if not sharpened.

So was it with him in yet another matter. Two minor officers, the armourer and captain of the hold, with whom he had never exchanged a word, his position on the ship not bringing him into contact with them; these men now for the first time began to cast upon Billy, when they chanced to encounter him, that peculiar glance which evidences that the man from whom it comes has been some way tampered with, and to the prejudice of him upon whom the glance lights. Never did it occur to Billy as a thing to be noted, or a thing suspicious, though he well knew the fact, that the armourer and captain of the hold, with the ship's yeoman, apothecary, and others of that grade, were by naval usage, messmates of the master-at-arms, men with ears convenient to his confidential tongue.

Our Handsome Sailor's manly forwardness upon occasion, and irresistible good-nature, indicating no mental superiority tending to excite an invidious feeling, bred general popularity, and this good-will on the part of most of his shipmates made him the less to concern himself about such mute aspects toward him as those whereto allusion has just been made.

As to the afterguardsman, though Billy for reasons already given necessarily saw little of him, yet when the two did happen to meet, invariably came the fellow's off-hand cheerful recognition, sometimes accompanied by a passing pleasant word or two. Whatever that equivocal young person's original design may really have been, or the design of which he might have been the deputy, certain it was from his manner upon these occasions, that he had wholly dropped it.

It was as if his precocity of crookedness (and every vulgar villain is precocious) had for once deceived him, and the man he had sought to entrap as a simpleton had, through his very simplicity, baffled him.

But shrewd ones may opine that it was hardly possible for Billy to refrain from going up to the afterguardsman and bluntly demanding to know his purpose in the initial interview, so abruptly closed in the fore-chains. Shrewd ones may also think it but natural in Billy to set about sounding some of the other impressed men of the ship in order to discover what basis, if any, there was for the emissary's obscure suggestions as to plotting disaffection aboard. Yes, the shrewd may so think. But something more, or rather, something else than mere shrewdness is perhaps needful for the due understanding of such a character as Billy Budd's.

As to Claggart, the monomania in the man—if that indeed it were—as involuntarily disclosed by starts in the manifestations detailed, yet in general covered over by his self-contained and rational demeanour; this, like a subterranean fire, was eating its way deeper and deeper in him. Something decisive must come of it.

XVI

After the mysterious interview in the fore-chains, the one so abruptly ended there by Billy, nothing especially germane to the story occurred until the events now about to be narrated.

Elsewhere it has been said that owing to the lack of frigates (of course better sailers than line-of-battle ships) in the English squadron up the Straits at that period, the *Indomitable* seventy-four was occasionally employed not only as an available substitute for a scout, but at times on detached service of more important kind. This was not alone because of her sailing qualities, not common in a ship of her rate, but quite as much probably, that the character of her commander, it was thought, especially adapted him for any duty where under unforeseen difficulties a prompt initiative might have to be taken in some matter demanding knowledge and ability in addition to those qualities employed in good seamanship. It was on an expedition of the latter sort, a somewhat distant one, and when the *Indomitable* was almost at her furthest remove from the fleet, that in the latter part of an afternoon-watch she unexpectedly came in sight of a ship of the enemy. It proved to be a frigate. The latter, perceiving through the glass that the weight of men and metal would be heavily against her, invoking her light heels, crowded sail to get away. After a chase urged almost against hope, and lasting until about the middle of the first dog-watch, she signally succeeded in effecting her escape.

Not long after the pursuit had been given up, and ere the excitement incident thereto had altogether waned away, the master-at-arms, ascending from his cavernous sphere, made his appearance cap in hand by the mainmast, respectfully waiting the notice of Captain Vere, then solitary walking the weather-side of the quarter-deck, doubtless somewhat chafed at the failure of the pursuit. The spot where Claggart stood was the place allotted to men of lesser grades seeking some more particular interview either with the officer of the deck or the captain himself. But from

hate toward one man - passion -
envy, jealousy, pale ire - natural
depravity.

the latter it was not often that a sailor or petty officer of those days would seek a hearing; only some exceptional cause would, according to established custom, have warranted that.

Presently, just as the commander, absorbed in his reflections, was on the point of turning aft in his promenade, he became sensible of Claggart's presence, and saw the doffed cap held in deferential expectancy. Here be it said that Captain Vere's personal knowledge of this petty officer had only begun at the time of the ship's last sailing from home, Claggart then for the first time, in transfer from a ship detained for repairs, supplying on board the *Indomitable* the place of a previous master-at-arms disabled and ashore.

No sooner did the commander observe who it was that now so deferentially stood awaiting his notice, than a peculiar expression came over his face. It was not unlike that which uncontrollably will flit across the countenance of one at unawares encountering a person who though known to him indeed has hardly been long enough known for thorough knowledge, but something in whose aspect nevertheless now for the first provokes a vaguely repellent distaste. But coming to a stand, and resuming much of his wonted official manner save that a sort of impatience lurked in the intonation of the opening word, he said, "Well, what is it, master-at-arms?"

With the air of a subordinate grieved at the necessity of being a messenger of ill-tidings, and while conscientiously determined to be frank, yet equally resolved upon shunning overstatement, Claggart at this invitation, or rather summons to disburthen, spoke up. What he said, conveyed in the language of no uneducated man, was to the effect following, if not altogether in these words, namely: That during the chase and preparations for the possible encounter he had seen enough to convince him that at least one sailor aboard was a dangerous character in a ship mustering some who not only had taken a guilty part in the late serious trouble, but others also who, like the man in question, had entered His Majesty's service under another form than enlistment.

Special services-detached fleet.

At this point Captain Vere with some impatience interrupted him:

"Be direct, man; say impressed men."

He was a good captain

Claggart made a gesture of subserviance and proceeded. Quite lately he (Claggart) had begun to suspect that some sort of movement prompted by the sailor in question was covertly going on, but he had not thought himself warranted in reporting the suspicion so long as it remained indistinct. But from what he had that afternoon observed in the man referred to, the suspicion of something clandestine going on had advanced to a point less removed from certainty. He deeply felt, he added, the serious responsibility assumed in making a report involving such possible consequences to the individual mainly concerned, besides tending to augment those natural anxieties which every naval commander must feel in view of extraordinary outbreaks so recent as those which, he sorrowfully said it, it needed not to name.

so it was a good ship.

Now at the first broaching of the matter Captain Vere, taken by surprise, could not wholly dissemble his disquietude, but as Claggart went on, the former's aspect changed into restiveness under something in the testifier's manner in giving his testimony. However, he refrained from interrupting him. And Claggart, continuing, concluded with this:

"God forbid, your honour, that the *Indomitable's* should be the experience of the——"

"Never mind that!" here peremptorily broke in the superior, his face altering with anger instantly, divining the ship that the other was about to name, one in which the Nore Mutiny had assumed a singularly tragical character that for a time jeopardised the life of its commander. Under the circumstances he was indignant at the purposed allusion. When the commissioned officers themselves were on all occasions very heedful how they referred to the recent event, for a petty officer unnecessarily to allude to it in the presence of his captain, this struck him as a most immodest presumption. Besides, to his quick sense of self-respect, it even looked under the circumstances something like an attempt to alarm him. Nor at that was he without some surprise that one who, so far as he had hitherto come

under his notice, had shown considerable tact in his function, should in this particular evince such lack of it.

But these thoughts and kindred dubious ones flitting
across his mind were suddenly replaced by an intuitional
surmise, which though as yet obscure in form, served practically to affect his reception of the ill tidings. Certain it is,
that long versed in everything pertaining to the complicated
gun-deck life, which like every other form of life has its
secret mines and dubious side, the side popularly dis-
claimed, Captain Vere did not permit himself to be unduly
disturbed by the general tenor of his subordinate's report.
Furthermore, if in view of recent events prompt action
should be taken at the first palpable sign of recurring insubordination, for all that, not judicious would it be, he
thought, to keep the idea of lingering disaffection alive by
undue forwardness in crediting an informer, even if his own
subordinate, and charged among other honours with police
surveillance of the crew. This feeling would not perhaps
have so prevailed with him were it not that upon a prior
occasion the patriotic zeal officially evinced by Claggart
had somewhat irritated him as appearing rather supersensi-
tive and strained. Furthermore, something even in the official's self-possessed and somewhat ostentatious manner in
making his specifications strangely reminded him of a
bandsman, a perjured witness in a capital case before a
court-martial ashore of which when a lieutenant he, Captain Vere, had been a member.

Now the peremptory check given to Claggart in the mat-
ter of the arrested allusion was quickly followed up by this:
"You say that there is at least one dangerous man aboard.
Name him."

"William Budd, a foretopman, your honour."

"William Budd!" repeated Captain Vere with unfeigned
astonishment; "and mean you the man that Lieutenant
Ratcliffe took from the merchantman not very long ago—
the young fellow who seems to be so popular with the men
—Billy, the Handsome Sailor, as they call him?"

"The same, your honour; but for all his youth and good
looks, a deep one. Not for nothing does he insinuate himself into the good-will of his shipmates, since at the least

they will at a pinch say a good word for him at all hazards. Did Lieutenant Ratcliffe happen to tell your honour of that adroit fling of Budd's jumping up in the cutter's bow under the merchantman's stern when he was being taken off? That sort of good humoured air even masks that at heart he resents his impressment. You have but noted his fair cheek. A mantrap may be under his ruddy-tipped daisies."

Now the *Handsome Sailor* as a signal figure among the crew had naturally enough attracted the captain's attention from the first. Though in general not very demonstrative to his officers, he had congratulated Lieutenant Ratcliffe upon his good fortune in lighting on such a fine specimen of the *genus homo,* who in the nude might have passed for a statue of young Adam before the Fall.

As to Billy's adieu to the ship *Rights-of-Man,* which the boarding lieutenant, in a deferential way, had indeed reported to him, Captain Vere, more as a good story than aught else (having mistakenly understood it as a satiric sally), had but thought so much the better of the impressed man for it; as a military sailor, admiring the spirit that could take an arbitrary enlistment so merrily and sensibly. The foretopman's conduct, too, so far as it had fallen under the captain's notice, had confirmed the first happy augury, while the new recruit's qualities as a *sailorman* seemed to be such that he had thought of recommending him to the executive officer for promotion to a place that would more frequently bring him under his own observation, namely, the captaincy of the mizzen-top, replacing there in the starboard-watch a man not so young whom partly for that reason he deemed less fitted for the post. Be it parenthesised here that since the mizzen-topmen have not to handle such breadths of heavy canvas as the lower sails on the mainmast and foremast, a young man if of the right stuff not only seems best adapted to duty there, but, in fact, is generally selected for the captaincy of that top, and the company under him are light hands, and often but strip-lings. In sum, Captain Vere had from the beginning deemed Billy Budd to be what in the naval parlance of the time was called a *"King's bargain,"* that is to say, for His Britannic Majesty's Navy a capital investment at small outlay or none at all.

After a brief pause, during which the reminiscences above mentioned passed vividly through his mind, he weighed the import of Claggart's last suggestion conveyed in the phrase "a mantrap under his ruddy-tipped daisies," and the more he weighed it the less reliance he felt in the informer's good faith. Suddenly he turned upon him: "Do you come to me, master-at-arms, with so foggy a tale? As to Budd, cite me an act or spoken word of his confirmatory of what you in general charge against him. Stay," drawing nearer to him, "heed what you speak. Just now and in a case like this, there is a yard-arm-end for the false witness."

"Ah, your honour!" sighed Claggart, mildly shaking his shapely head as in sad deprecation of such unmerited severity of tone. Then bridling, erecting himself as in virtuous self-assertion, he circumstantially alleged certain words and acts which collectively, if credited, led to presumptions mortally inculpating Budd, and for some of these averments, he added, substantiating proof was not far.

With grey eyes impatient and distrustful, essaying to fathom to the bottom Claggart's calm violet ones, Captain Vere again heard him out; then for the moment stood ruminating. Claggart—himself for the time liberated from the other's scrutiny—steadily regarded Captain Vere with a look difficult to render—a look curious of the operation of his tactics, a look such as might have been that of the spokesman of the envious children of Jacob deceptively imposing upon the troubled patriarch the blood-dyed coat of young Joseph.

Though something exceptional in the moral quality of Captain Vere made him, in earnest encounter with a fellow-man, a veritable touchstone of that man's essential nature, yet now as to Claggart and what was really going on in him, his feeling partook less of intuitional conviction than of strong suspicion clogged by strange dubieties. The perplexity he evinced proceeded less from aught touching the man informed against—as Claggart doubtless opined —than from considerations how best to act in regard to the informer. At first, indeed, he was naturally for summoning that substantiation of his allegations which Claggart said was at hand. But such a proceeding would result in the matter at once getting abroad, which in the present stage of it, he thought, might undesirably affect the ship's company. If Claggart was a false witness—that closed the affair. And therefore, before trying the accusation, he would first practically test the accuser; and he thought this could be done in a quiet undemonstrative way.

The measure he determined upon involved a shifting of the scene, a transfer to a place less exposed to observation than the broad quarter-deck. For although the few gun-room officers there at the time had, in due observance of naval etiquette, withdrawn to leeward the moment Captain Vere had begun his promenade on the deck's weather-side; and though during the colloquy with Claggart they of course ventured not to diminish the distance; and though throughout the interview Captain Vere's voice was far from high, and Claggart's silvery and low; and the wind in the cordage and the wash of the sea helped the more to put them beyond ear-shot; nevertheless, the interviewer's continuance already had attracted observation from some topmen aloft, and other sailors in the waist or farther forward.

Having determined upon his measures, Captain Vere forthwith took action. Abruptly turning to Claggart he asked, "Master-at-arms, is it now Budd's watch aloft?"

"No, your honour."

Whereupon, "Mr. Wilkes," summoning the nearest midshipman, "tell Albert to come to me." Albert was the captain's hammock-boy, a sort of sea-valet, in whose discretion and fidelity his master had much confidence. The lad appeared. "You know Budd, the foretopman?"

"I do, sir."

"Go find him. It is his watch off. Manage to tell him out of ear-shot that he is wanted aft. Contrive it that he speaks to nobody. Keep him in talk yourself. And not till you get well aft here, not till then, let him know that the place where he is wanted is my cabin. You understand? Go. Master-at-arms, show yourself on the decks below, and

when you think it time for Albert to be coming with his
man, stand by quietly to follow the sailor in."

XVII

Now when the foretopman found himself closeted, as it
were, in the cabin with the captain and Claggart, he was
surprised enough. But it was a surprise unaccompanied by
apprehension or distrust. To an immature nature, essentially honest and humane, forewarning intimations of subtler danger from one's kind came tardily, if at all. The only
thing that took shape in the young sailor's mind was this:
"Yes, the captain, I have always thought, looks kindly
upon me. Wonder if he's going to make me his coxswain.
I should like that. And maybe now he is going to ask the
master-at-arms about me."

"Shut the door there, sentry," said the commander.
"Stand without and let nobody come in. Now, master-at-
arms, tell this man to his face what you told of him to
me"; and stood prepared to scrutinise the mutually con-
fronting visages.

With the measured step and calm collected air of an
asylum physician approaching in the public hall some patient beginning to show indications of a coming paroxysm,
Claggart deliberately advanced within short range of Billy,
and mesmerically looking him in the eye, briefly recapitu-
lated the accusation.

Not at first did Billy take it in. When he did the rose-
tan of his cheek looked struck as by white leprosy. He stood
like one impaled and gagged. Meanwhile the accuser's eyes,
removing not as yet from the blue, dilated ones, underwent
a phenomenal change, their wonted rich violet colour blur-
ring into a muddy purple. Those lights of human intelligence losing human expression, gelidly protruding like the
alien eyes of certain uncatalogued creatures of the deep.

The first mesmeric glance was one of surprised fascination; the last was as the hungry lurch of the torpedo-fish.

"Speak, man!" said Captain Vere to the transfixed one,
struck by his aspect even more than by Claggart's. "Speak!

defend yourself." Which appeal caused but a strange, dumb gesturing and gurgling in Billy; amazement at such an accusation so suddenly sprung on inexperienced nonage; this, and it may be horror at the accuser, serving to bring out his lurking defect, and in this instance for the time intensifying it into a convulsed tongue-tie; while the intent head and entire form, straining forward in an agony of ineffectual eagerness to obey the injunction to speak and defend himself, gave an expression to the face like that of a condemned vestal priestess in the moment of being buried alive, and in the first struggle against suffocation.

Though at the time Captain Vere was quite ignorant of Billy's liability to vocal impediment, he now immediately divined it, since vividly Billy's aspect recalled to him that of a bright young schoolmate of his whom he had seen struck by much the same startling impotence in the act of eagerly rising in the class to be foremost in response to a testing question put to it by the master. Going close up to the young sailor, and laying a soothing hand on his shoulder, he said, "There is no hurry, my boy. Take your time, take your time." Contrary to the effect intended, these words, so fatherly in tone, doubtless touching Billy's heart to the quick, prompted yet more violent efforts at utterance —efforts soon ending for the time in confirming the paralysis, and bringing to the face an expression which was as a crucifixion to behold. The next instant, quick as the flame from a discharged cannon at night, his right arm shot out, and Claggart dropped to the deck. Whether intentionally, or but owing to the young athlete's superior height, the blow had taken effect full upon the forehead, so shapely an intellectual-looking a feature in the master-at-arms; so that the body fell over lengthwise, like a heavy plank tilted from erectness. A gasp or two, and he lay motionless.

"Fated boy," breathed Captain Vere, in tone so low as to be almost a whisper, "what have you done! But here, help me."

The twain raised the felled one from the loins up into a sitting position. The spare form flexibly acquiesced, but inertly. It was like handling a dead snake. They lowered it back. Regaining erectness, Captain Vere with one hand

covering his face stood to all appearance as impassive as
the object at his feet. Was he absorbed in taking in all the
bearings of the event, and what was best not only now at
once to be done, but also in the sequel? Slowly he uncov-
ered his face; and the effect was as if the moon emerging
from eclipse should reappear with quite another aspect than
that which had gone into hiding. The father in him, manifested towards Billy thus far in the scene, was replaced by
the military disciplinarian. In his official tone he bade the
foretopman retire to a state-room aft (pointing it out), and
there remain till thence summoned. This order Billy in silence mechanically obeyed. Then going to the cabin door
where it opened on the quarter-deck, Captain Vere said to
the sentry without, "Tell somebody to send Albert here."
When the lad appeared his master so contrived it that he
should not catch sight of the prone one. "Albert," he said
to him, "tell the surgeon I wish to see him. You need not
come back till called."

When the surgeon entered—a self-poised character of
that grave sense and experience that hardly anything could
take him aback—Captain Vere advanced to meet him, thus
unconsciously interrupting his view of Claggart, and interrupting the other's wonted unceremonious salutation said,
"Nay, tell me how it is with yonder man," directing his attention to the prostrate one.

The surgeon looked, and for all his self-command, somewhat startled at the abrupt revelation. On Claggart's always pallid complexion thick black blood was now oozing
from mouth and ear. To the gazer's professional eyes it was
unmistakably no living man that he saw.

"Is it so, then?" said Captain Vere, intently watching
him. "I thought it. But verify it." Whereupon the customary tests confirmed the surgeon's first glance, who
now looking up in unfeigned concern, cast a look of intense
inquisitiveness upon his superior. But Captain Vere, with
one hand to his brow, was standing motionless. Suddenly,
catching the surgeon's arm convulsively, he exclaimed,
pointing down to the body, "It is the divine judgment of
Ananias! Look!"

Disturbed by the excited manner he had never before

observed in the *Indomitable's* captain, and as yet wholly ignorant of the affair, the prudent surgeon nevertheless held his peace, only again looking an earnest interrogation as to what it was that had resulted in such a tragedy.

But Captain Vere was now again motionless, standing absorbed in thought. But again starting, he vehemently exclaimed, "Struck dead by an angel of God. Yet the angel must hang!"

At these interjections, incoherences to the listener as yet unapprised of the antecedent events, the surgeon was profoundly discomforted. But now, as recollecting himself, Captain Vere in less harsh tone briefly related the circumstances leading up to the event.

"But come; we must dispatch," he added; "help me to remove him (meaning the body) to yonder compartment" —designating one opposite where the foretopman remained immured. Anew disturbed by a request that as implying a desire for secrecy seemed unaccountably strange to him, there was nothing for the subordinate to do but comply.

"Go now," said Captain Vere, with something of his wonted manner, "go now. I shall presently call a drumhead court. Tell the lieutenants what has happened, and tell Mr. Morton"—meaning the captain of marines. "And charge them to keep the matter to themselves."

Full of disquietude and misgivings, the surgeon left the cabin. Was Captain Vere suddenly affected in his mind, or was it but a transient excitement brought about by so strange and extraordinary a happening? As to the drumhead court, it struck the surgeon as impolitic, if nothing more. The thing to do, he thought, was to place Billy Budd in confinement, and in a way dictated by usage, and postpone further action in so extraordinary a case to such time as they should again join the squadron, and then transfer it to the admiral. He recalled the unwonted agitation of Captain Vere and his excited exclamations, so at variance with his normal manner. Was he unhinged? But assuming that he was, it were not so susceptible of proof. What then could he do? No more trying situation is conceivable than that of an officer subordinated under a captain whom he suspects to be, not mad indeed, but yet not quite unaffected in his intellect. To argue his order to him would be insolence. To resist him would be mutiny. In obedience to Captain Vere he communicated to the lieutenants and captain of marines what had happened, saying nothing more as to the captain's state. They stared at him in surprise and concern. Like him, they seemed to think that such a matter should be reported to the admiral.

Who in the rainbow can draw the line where the violet tint ends and the orange tint begins? Distinctly we see the difference of the colour, but where exactly does the first one visibly enter into the other? So with sanity and insanity. In pronounced cases there is no question about them. But in some cases, in various degrees supposedly less pronounced, to draw the line of demarcation few will undertake, though for a fee some professional experts will. There is nothing nameable but that some men will undertake to do for pay. In other words, there are instances where it is next to impossible to determine whether a man is sane or beginning to be otherwise.

Whether Captain Vere, as the surgeon professionally surmised, was really the sudden victim of any degree of aberration, one must determine for himself by such light as this narrative may afford.

XVIII

The unhappy event which has been narrated could not have happened at a worse juncture. For it was close on the heel of the suppressed insurrections, an after-time very critical to naval authority, demanding from every English sea-commander two qualities not readily interfusable—prudence and rigour. Moreover, there was something crucial in the case.

In the jugglery of circumstances preceding and attending the event on board the *Indomitable,* and in the light of that martial code whereby it was formally to be judged, innocence and guilt, personified in Claggart and Budd, in effect changed places.

In the legal view, the apparent victim of the tragedy

was he who had sought to victimise a man blameless; and
the indisputable deed of the latter, navally regarded, constituted the most heinous of military crimes. Yet more.
The essential right and wrong involved in the matter, the
clearer that might be, so much the worse for the responsibility of a loyal sea-commander, inasmuch as he was authorised to determine the matter on that primitive legal
basis.

Small wonder then that the *Indomitable's* captain,
though in general a man of rigid decision, felt that circum-
spectness not less than promptitude was necessary. Until
he could decide upon his course, and in each detail, and
not only so, but until the concluding measure was upon
the point of being enacted, he deemed it advisable, in view
of all the circumstances, to guard as much as possible
against publicity. Here he may or may not have erred.
Certain it is, however, that subsequently in the confidential
talk of more than one or two gun-rooms and cabins he was
not a little criticised by some officers, a fact imputed by
his friends, and vehemently by his cousin Jack Denton, to
professional jealousy of Starry Vere. Some imaginative
ground for invidious comment there was. The maintenance
of secrecy in the matter, the confining all knowledge of it
for a time to the place where the homicide occurred—the
quarter-deck cabin; in these particulars lurked some re-
semblance to the policy adopted in those tragedies of the
palace which have occurred more than once in the capital
founded by Peter the Barbarian, great chiefly by his crimes.

The case was such that fain would the *Indomitable's*
captain have deferred taking any action whatever respect-
ing it further than to keep the foretopman a close prisoner
till the ship rejoined the squadron, and then submitting the
matter to the judgment of his admiral.

But a true military officer is in one particular like a true
monk. Not with more of self-abnegation will the latter
keep his vows of monastic obedience than the former his
vows of allegiance to martial duty.

Feeling that unless quick action was taken on it, the
deed of the foretopman, as soon as it should be known on
the gun-decks, would tend to awaken any slumbering em-

bers of the Nore among the crew, a sense of the urgency
of the case overruled in Captain Vere every other consideration. But though a conscientious disciplinarian he was
no lover of authority for mere authority's sake. Very far
was he from embracing opportunities for monopolising to
himself the perils of moral responsibility, none at least that
could properly be referred to an official superior, or shared
with him by his official equals, or even subordinates. So
thinking, he was glad it would not be at variance with
usage to turn the matter over to a summary court of his
own officers, reserving to himself as the one on whom the
ultimate accountability would rest, the right of maintaining a supervision of it, or formally or informally inter-
posing at need. Accordingly a drum-head court was summarily convened, he electing the individuals composing it
—the first lieutenant, the captain of marines, and the
sailing-master.

In associating an officer of marines with the sea-lieu-
tenant in a case having to do with a sailor, the commander
perhaps deviated from general custom. He was prompted
thereto by the circumstances that he took that soldier to
be a judicious person, thoughtful and not altogether incapable of grappling with a difficult case unprecedented in
his prior experience. Yet even as to him he was not without some latent misgiving, for withal he was an extremely
good-natured man, an enjoyer of his dinner, a sound
sleeper, and inclined to obesity. The sort of man who,
though he would always maintain his manhood in battle,
might not prove altogether reliable in a moral dilemma involving aught of the tragic. As to the first lieutenant and
the sailing-master, Captain Vere could not but be aware
that though honest natures, of approved gallantry upon
occasion, their intelligence was mostly confined to the matter of active seamanship, and the fighting demands of their
profession. The court was held in the same cabin where
the unfortunate affair had taken place. This cabin, the commander's, embraced the entire area under the poop-deck.
Aft, and on either side, was a small state-room—the one
room temporarily a jail, and the other a dead-house—and
a yet smaller compartment leaving a space between, ex-

panding forward into a goodly oblong of length coinciding
with the ship's beam. A skylight of moderate dimensions
was overhead, and at each end of the oblong space were
two sashed port-hole windows easily convertible back into
embrasures for short carronades.

All being quickly in readiness, Billy Budd was arraigned,
Captain Vere necessarily appearing as the sole witness in
the case, and as such temporarily sinking his rank, though
singularly maintaining it in a matter apparently trivial,
namely, that he testified from the ship's weather-side, with
that object having caused the court to sit on the lee-side.
Concisely he narrated all that had led up to the catastrophe,
omitting nothing in Claggart's accusation, and deposing as
to the manner in which the prisoner had received it. At
this testimony the three officers glanced with no little surprise at Billy Budd, the last man they would have suspected, either of mutinous design alleged by Claggart, or
of the undeniable deed he himself had done. The first lieutenant taking judicial primary, and turning toward the
prisoner, said, "Captain Vere has spoken. Is it or is it not
as Captain Vere says?" In response came syllables not so
much impeded in the utterances as might have been anticipated. They were these:—

"Captain Vere tells the truth. It is just as Captain Vere
says, but it is not as the master-at-arms said. I have eaten
the King's bread, and I am true to the King."

"I believe you, my man," said the witness, his voice indicating a suppressed emotion not otherwise betrayed.

"God will bless you for that, your honour!" not without
stammering, said Billy, and all but broke down. But immediately was recalled to self-control by another question, to
which with the same emotional difficulty of utterance he
said, "No, there was no malice between us. I never bore
malice against the master-at-arms. I am sorry that he is
dead. I did not mean to kill him. Could I have used my
tongue I would not have struck him. But he foully lied to
my face, and in the presence of my captain, and I had to
say something, and I could only say it with a blow. God
help me!"

In the impulsive above-board manner of the frank one

the court saw confirmed all that was implied in words that just previously had perplexed them, coming as they did from the testifier to the tragedy, and promptly following Billy's impassioned disclaimer of mutinous intent—Captain Vere's words, "I believe you, my man."

Next, it was asked of him whether he knew of or suspected aught savouring of incipient trouble (meaning mutiny, though the explicit term was avoided) going on in any section of the ship's company.

The reply lingered. This was naturally imputed by the court to the same vocal embarrassment which had retarded or obstructed previous answers. But in main it was otherwise here; the question immediately recalling to Billy's mind the interview with the afterguardsman in the forechains. But an innate repugnance to playing a part at all approaching that of an informer against one's own shipmates—the same erring sense of uninstructed honour which had stood in the way of his reporting the matter at the time, though as a loyal man-of-war's man it was incumbent on him, and failure so to do it, charged against him and proven, would have subjected him to the heaviest of penalties. This, with the blind feeling now his, that nothing really was being hatched, prevailed with him. When the answer came it was a negative.

"One question more," said the officer of marines now first speaking, and with a troubled earnestness. "You tell us that what the master-at-arms said against you was a lie. Now why should he have so lied, so maliciously lied, since you declare there was no malice between you?"

At that question, unintentionally touching on a spiritual sphere, wholly obscure to Billy's thoughts, he was nonplussed, evincing a confusion indeed that some observers such as can be imagined, would have construed into involuntary evidence of hidden guilt. Nevertheless he strove some way to answer, but all at once relinquished the vain endeavour, at the same time turning an appealing glance towards Captain Vere, as deeming him his best helper and friend. Captain Vere, who had been seated for a time, rose to his feet, addressing the interrogator. "The question you put to him comes naturally enough. But how can he rightly answer it, or anybody else? unless indeed it be he who lies within there," designating the compartment where lay the corpse. "But the prone one there will not rise to our summons. In effect though, as it seems to me, the point you make is hardly material. Quite aside from any conceivable motive actuating the master-at-arms, and irrespective of the provocation of the blow, a martial court must needs in the present case confine its attention to the blow's consequence, which consequence is to be deemed not otherwise than as the striker's deed!"

This utterance, the full significance of which it was not at all likely that Billy took in, nevertheless caused him to turn a wistful, interrogative look toward the speaker, a look in its dumb expressiveness not unlike that which a dog of generous breed might turn upon his master, seeking in his face some elucidation of a previous gesture ambiguous to the canine intelligence. Nor was the same utterance without marked effect upon the three officers, more especially the soldier. Couched in it seemed to them a meaning unanticipated, involving a prejudgment on the speaker's part. It served to augment a mental disturbance previously evident enough.

The soldier once more spoke, in a tone of suggestive dubiety addressing at once his associates and Captain Vere: "Nobody is present—none of the ship's company, I mean, who might shed lateral light, if any is to be had, upon what remains mysterious in this matter."

"That is thoughtfully put," said Captain Vere; "I see your drift. Ay, there is a mystery; but to use a Scriptural phrase, it is 'a mystery of iniquity,' a matter for psychological theologians to discuss. But what has a military court to do with it? Not to add that for us, any possible investigation of it is cut off by the lasting tongue-tie—him—in yonder," again designating the mortuary state-room. "The prisoner's deed. With that alone we have to do."

To this, particularly the closing reiteration, the marine soldier, knowing not how aptly to reply, sadly abstained from saying aught. The first lieutenant, who at the outset had not unnaturally assumed primacy in the court, now over-rulingly instructed by a glance from Captain Vere, a glance more effective than words, resumed that primacy. Turning to the prisoner: "Budd," he said, and scarce in equable tones, "Budd, if you have aught further to say for yourself, say it now."

Upon this the young sailor turned another quick glance toward Captain Vere; then, as taking a hint from that aspect, a hint confirming his own instinct that silence was now best, replied to the lieutenant, "I have said all, sir."

The marine—the same who had been the sentinel without the cabin-door at the time that the foretopman, followed by the master-at-arms, entered it—he, standing by the sailor throughout their judicial proceedings, was now directed to take him back to the after-compartment originally assigned to the prisoner and his custodian. As the twain disappeared from view, the three officers, as partially liberated from some inward constraint associated with Billy's mere presence, simultaneously stirred in their seats. They exchanged looks of troubled indecision, yet feeling that decide they must and without long delay, for Captain Vere was for the time sitting unconsciously with his back toward them, apparently in one of his absent fits, gazing out from a sashed port-hole to windward upon the monotonous blank of the twilight sea. But the court's silence continuing, broken only at moments by brief consultations in low, earnest tones, this seemed to assure him and encourage him. Turning, he to and fro paced the cabin athwart; in the returning ascent to windward, climbing the slant deck in the ship's lee roll; without knowing it symbolising thus in his action a mind resolute to surmount difficulties even if against primitive instincts strong as the wind and the sea. Presently he came to a stand before the three. After scanning their faces he stood less as mustering his thoughts for expression, than as one only deliberating how best to put them to well-meaning men not intellectually mature, men with whom it was necessary to demonstrate certain principles that were axioms to himself. Similar impatience as to talking is perhaps one reason that deters some minds from addressing any popular assemblies; under which head is to be classed most legislatures in a democracy.

When speak he did, something both in the substance of what he said and his manner of saying it, showed the influence of unshared studies modifying and tempering the practical training of an active career. This, along with his phraseology now and then, was suggestive of the grounds whereon rested that imputation of a certain pedantry socially alleged against him by certain naval men of wholly practical cast, captains who nevertheless would frankly concede that His Majesty's Navy mustered no more efficient officers of their grade than *Starry Vere*.

What he said was to this effect: "Hitherto I have been but the witness, little more; and I should hardly think now to take another tone, that of your coadjutor, for the time, did I not perceive in you—at the crisis too—a troubled hesitancy, proceeding, I doubt not, from the clashing of military duty with moral scruple—scruple vitalised by compassion. For the compassion, how can I otherwise but share it? But mindful of paramount obligation, I strive against scruples that may tend to enervate decision. Not, gentlemen, that I hide from myself that the case is an exceptional one. Speculatively regarded, it well might be referred to a jury of casuists. But for us here, acting not as casuists or moralists, it is a case practical and under martial law practically to be dealt with.

"But your scruples! Do they move as in a dusk? Challenge them. Make them advance and declare themselves. Come now: do they impart something like this: If, mindless of palliating circumstances, we are bound to regard the death of the master-at-arms as the prisoner's deed, then does that deed constitute a capital crime whereof the penalty is a mortal one? But in natural justice is nothing but the prisoner's overt act to be considered? Now can we adjudge to summary and shameful death a fellow-creature innocent before God, and whom we feel to be so?—Does that state it aright? You sign sad assent. Well, I too feel that, the full force of that. It is Nature. But do these buttons that we wear attest that our allegiance is to Nature? No, to the King. Though the ocean, which is inviolate Nature primeval, though this be the element where we move and have our being as sailors, yet as the King's officers lies our duty in a sphere correspondingly natural? So little is that true, that in receiving our commissions we in the most important regards ceased to be natural free agents. When war is declared, are we the commissioned fighters previously consulted? We fight at command. If our judgments approve the war, that is but coincidence. So in other particulars. So now, would it be so much we ourselves that would condemn as it would be martial law operating through us? For that law and the rigour of it, we are not responsible. Our vowed responsibility is in this: That however pitilessly that law may operate, we nevertheless adhere to it and administer it.

"But the exceptional in the matter moves the heart within you. Even so, too, is mine moved. But let not warm hearts betray heads that should be cool. Ashore in a criminal case will an upright judge allow himself off the bench to be waylaid by some tender kinswoman of the accused seeking to touch him with her tearful plea? Well, the heart here is as that piteous woman. The heart is the feminine in man, and hard though it be, she must here be ruled out."

He paused, earnestly studying them for a moment; then resumed.

"But something in your aspect seems to urge that it is not solely that heart that moves in you, but also the conscience, the private conscience. But tell me whether or not, occupying the position we do, private conscience should not yield to that imperial one formulated in the code under which alone we officially proceed?"

Here the three men moved in their seats, less convinced than agitated by the course of an argument troubling but the more the spontaneous conflict within. Perceiving which, the speaker paused for a moment; then abruptly changing his tone, went on.

"To steady us a bit, let us recur to the facts. In wartime at sea a man-of-war's man strikes his superior in grade, and the blow kills. Apart from its effect, the blow itself is, according to the Articles of War, a capital crime. Furthermore——"

"Ay, sir," emotionally broke in the officer of marines,

"in one sense it was. But surely Budd purposed neither mutiny nor homicide."

"Surely not, my good man. And before a court less arbitrary and more merciful than a martial one the plea would largely extenuate. At the Last Assizes it shy acquit. But how here? We proceed under the law (the Mutiny Act. In feature no child can resemble his her more than that Act resembles in spirit the thing from wch it derives—War. In His Majesty's service—in this p indeed—there are Englishmen forced to fight for the K against their will. Against their conscience, for aught know. Though as their fellow-creatures some of us n appreciate their position, yet as Navy officers, what re we of it? Still less recks the enemy. Our impressed men would fain cut down in the same swath with our voluntee As regards the enemy's naval conscripts, some of who may even share our own abhorrence of the regicidal Fren Directory, it is the same on our side. War looks but to th frontage, the appearance. And the Mutiny Act, War's child, takes after the father. Budd's intent or non-intent is nothing to the purpose.

"But while, put to it by those anxieties in you which I cannot but respect, I only repeat myself—while thus strangely we prolong proceedings that should be summary, the enemy may be sighted and an engagement result. We must do; and one of two things must we do—condemn or let go."

"Can we not convict and yet mitigate the penalty?" asked the junior lieutenant, here speaking, and falteringly, for the first.

"Lieutenant, were that clearly lawful for us under the circumstances, consider the consequences of such clemency. The people" (meaning the ship's company) "have native sense; most of them are familiar with our naval usage and tradition; and how would they take it? Even could you explain to them—which our official position forbids—they, long moulded by arbitrary discipline, have not that kind of intelligent responsiveness that might qualify them to comprehend and discriminate. No, to the people the foretopman's deed, however it be worded in the announcement, will be plain homicide committed in a flagrant act of mutiny. What penalty for that should follow, they know. But it does not follow. *Why?* they will ruminate. You know what sailors are. Will they not revert to the recent outbreak at the Nore? Ay, they know the well-founded alarm—the panic it struck throughout England. Our clement sentence they would account pusillanimous. They would think that we flinch, that we are afraid of them —afraid of practising a lawful rigour singularly demanded at this juncture lest it should provoke new troubles. What name to us such a conjecture on their part, and how deadly to discipline. You see then whither, prompted by duty and the law, I steadfastly drive. But I beseech you, my friends, do not take me amiss. I feel as you do for this unfortunate boy. But did he know our hearts, I take him to be of that generous nature that he would feel even for us on whom in this military necessity so heavy a compulsion is laid."

With that, crossing the deck, he resumed his place by the sashed port-hole, tacitly leaving the three to come to a decision. On the cabin's opposite side the troubled court sat silent. Loyal lieges, plain and practical, though at bottom they dissented from some points Captain Vere had put to them, they were without the faculty, hardly had the inclination to gainsay one whom they felt to be an earnest man, one, too, not less their superior in mind than in naval rank. But it is not improbable that even such of his words as were not without influence over them, came home to them less than his closing appeal to their instinct as sea-officers. He forecasted the practical consequences to discipline (considering the unconfirmed tone of the fleet at the time), if violent killing at sea by a man-of-war's man of a superior in grade were allowed to pass for aught else than a capital crime, and one demanding prompt infliction of the penalty.

Not unlikely they were brought to something more or less akin to that harassed frame of mind which in the year 1842 actuated the commander of the U.S. brig-of-war *Somers* to resolve—under the so-called Articles of War, articles modelled upon the English Mutiny Act—

upon the execution at sea of a midshipman and two petty officers as mutineers designing the seizure of the brig. This resolution was carried out, though in a time of peace and within not many days' sail of home, and vindicated by a naval court of inquiry subsequently convened ashore. History, and here cited without comment. True, the circumstances on board the *Somers* were different from those on board the *Indomitable*. But the urgency felt, well warranted or otherwise, was much the same.

Says a writer whom few know, "Forty years after a battle it is easy for a non-combatant to reason about how it ought to have been fought. It is another thing personally and under fire to direct the fighting while involved in the obscuring smoke of it. Much so with respect to other emergencies involving considerations both practical and moral, and when it is imperative promptly to act. The greater the fog the more it imperils the steamer, and speed is put on though at the hazard of running somebody down. Little ween the snug card-players in the cabin of the responsibilities of the sleepless man on the bridge."

In brief, Billy Budd was formally convicted and sentenced to be hung at the yard-arm in the early morning-watch, it being now night. Otherwise, as is customary in such cases, the sentence would forthwith have been carried out. In war-time on the field or in the fleet, a mortal punishment decreed by a drum-head court—on the field sometimes decreed by but a nod from the general—follows without delay on the heel of conviction without appeal.

Hung on Main Mast

XIX

his fallession

It was Captain Vere himself who of his own motion communicated the finding of the court to the prisoner; for that purpose going to the compartment where he was in custody, and bidding the marine there to withdraw for the time.

Beyond the communication of the sentence what took place at this interview was never known. But, in view of the character of the twain briefly closeted in that stateroom, each radically sharing in the rarer qualities of one

"God bless Captain Vere."

nature—so rare, indeed, as to be all but incredible to average minds, however much cultivated—some conjectures may be ventured.

It would have been in consonance with the spirit of Captain Vere should he on this occasion have concealed nothing from the condemned one; should he indeed have frankly disclosed to him the part he himself had played in bringing about the decision, at the same time revealing his actuated motives. On Billy's side it is not improbable that such a confession would have been received in much the same spirit that prompted it. Not without a sort of joy indeed he might have appreciated the brave opinion of him implied in his captain making such a confidant of him. Nor as to the sentence itself could he have been insensible that it was imparted to him as to one not afraid to die. Even more may have been. Captain Vere in the end may have developed the passion sometimes latent under an exterior stoical or indifferent. He was old enough to have been Billy's father. The austere devotee of military duty, letting himself melt back into what remains primeval in our formalised humanity, may in the end have caught Billy to his heart, even as Abraham may have caught young Isaac on the brink of resolutely offering him up in obedience to the exacting behest. But there is no telling the sacrament—seldom if in any case revealed to the gadding world wherever, under circumstances at all akin to those here attempted to be set forth, two of great Nature's nobler order embrace. There is privacy at the time, inviolable to the survivor, and holy oblivion, the sequel to each diviner magnanimity, providentially covers all at last.

The first to encounter Captain Vere in the act of leaving the compartment was the senior lieutenant. The face he beheld, for the moment one expressive of the agony of the strong, was to that officer, though a man of fifty, a startling revelation. That the condemned one suffered less than he who mainly had affected the condemnation, was apparently indicated by the former's exclamation in the scene soon perforce to be touched upon.

Of a series of incidents within a brief term rapidly following each other the adequate narration may take up a term less brief, especially if explanation or comment here and there seem requisite to the better understanding of such incidents. Between the entrance into the cabin of him who never left it alive, and him who when he did leave it left it as one condemned to die; between this and the closeted interview just given, less than an hour and a half had elapsed. It was an interval long enough, however, to awaken speculations among no few of the ship's company as to what it was that could be detaining in the cabin the master-at-arms and the sailor, for it was rumoured that both of them had been seen to enter it, and neither of them had been seen to emerge. This rumour had got abroad upon the gun-decks and in the tops; the people of a great warship being in one respect like villagers, taking microscopic note of every untoward movement or non-movement going on. When therefore in weather not at all tempestuous all hands were called in the second dog-watch, a summons under such circumstances not usual in those hours, the crew were not wholly unprepared for some announcement extraordinary, one having connection, too, with the continued absence of the two men from their wonted haunts.

There was a moderate sea at the time; and the moon newly risen, and near to being at its full, silvered the white spar-deck wherever not blotted by the clear-cut shadows horizontally thrown of fixtures and moving men. On either side the quarter-deck the marine guard under arms was drawn up; and Captain Vere, standing in his place surrounded by all the ward-room officers, addressed his men. In so doing his manner showed neither more nor less than that properly pertaining to his supreme position aboard his own ship. In clear terms and concise he told them what had taken place in the cabin; that the master-at-arms was dead; that he who had killed him had been already tried by a summary court and condemned to death; and that the execution would take place in the early morning watch. The word *mutiny* was not named in what he said. He refrained, too, from making the occasion an opportunity for any preachment as to the maintenance of discipline, thinking, perhaps, that under existing circumstances in the Navy the consequence of violating discipline should be made to speak for itself.

Their captain's announcement was listened to by the throng of standing sailors in a dumbness like that of a seated congregation of believers in Hell listening to their clergyman's announcement of his Calvinistic text.

At the close, however, a confused murmur went up. It began to wax all but instantly, then at a sign, was pierced and suppressed by shrill whistles of the boatswain and his mates piping, "Down one watch."

To be prepared for burial Claggart's body was delivered to certain petty officers of his mess. And here, not to clog the sequel with lateral matter, it may be added that at a suitable hour, the master-at-arms was committed to the sea with every funeral honour properly belonging to his naval grade.

In this proceeding, as in every public one growing out of the tragedy, strict adherence to usage was observed. Nor in any point could it have been at all deviated from, either with respect to Claggart or Billy Budd, without begetting undesirable speculations in the ship's company, sailors, and more particularly man-of-war's men, being of all men the greatest sticklers for usage.

For similar cause all communication between Captain Vere and the condemned ended with the closeted interview already given, the latter being now surrendered to the ordinary routine preliminary to the end. This transfer under guard from the captain's quarters was effected without unusual precautions—at least no visible ones.

If possible, not to let the men so much as surmise that their officers anticipate aught amiss from them, is the tacit rule in a military ship. And the more that some sort of trouble should really be apprehended, the more do the officers keep that apprehension to themselves; though not the less unostentatious vigilance may be augmented.

In the present instance the sentry placed over the prisoner had strict orders to let no one have communications with him but the chaplain. And certain unobtrusive measures were taken absolutely to ensure this point.

XX

In a seventy-four of the old order the deck known as the upper gun-deck was the one covered over by the spar-deck, which last, though not without its armament, was for the most part exposed to the weather. In general it was at all hours free from hammocks; those of the crew swinging on the lower gun-deck and berth-deck, the latter being not only a dormitory but also the place for the stowing of the sailors' bags, and on both sides lined with the large chests or movable pantries of the many messes of the men.

On the starboard side of the *Indomitable's* upper gun-deck, behold Billy Budd under sentry lying prone in irons, in one of the bays formed by the regular spacing of the guns comprising the batteries on either side. All these pieces were of the heavier calibre of that period. Mounted on lumbering wooden carriages, they were hampered with cumbersome harness of breeching and strong side-tackles for running them out. Guns and carriages, together with the long rammers and shorter lintstocks lodged in loops overhead—all these, as customary, were painted black; and the heavy hempen breechings tarred to the same tint, wore the like livery of the undertaker. In contrast with the funereal tone of these surroundings the prone sailor's exterior apparel, white *jumper* and white duck trousers, each more or less soiled, dimly glimmered in the obscure light of the bay like a patch of discoloured snow in early April lingering at some upland cave's black mouth. In effect he is already in his shroud or the garments that shall serve him in lieu of one. Over him, but scarce illuminating him, two battle-lanterns swing from two massive beams of the deck above. Fed with the oil supplied by the war-contractors (whose gains, honest or otherwise, are in every land an anticipated portion of the harvest of death) with flickering splashes of dirty yellow light they pollute the pale moonshine all but ineffectually struggling in obstructed flecks through the open ports from which the tompioned cannon protrude. Other lanterns at intervals serve but to bring out somewhat the obscurer bays which, like small

confessionals or side-chapels in a cathedral, branch from
the long, dim-vista'd, broad aisle, between the two batteries of that covered tier.

Such was the deck where now lay the Handsome Sailor.
Through the rose-tan of his complexion, no pallor could
have shown. It would have taken days of sequestration
from the winds and the sun to have brought about the ef-
facement of that. But the skeleton in the cheek-bone at
the point of its angle was just beginning delicately to be
defined under the warm-tinted skin. In fervid hearts self-
contained some brief experiences devour our human tissue
as secret fire in a ship's hold consumes cotton in the bale.

But now, lying between the two guns, as nipped in the
vice of fate, Billy's agony, mainly proceeding from a generous young heart's virgin experience of the diabolical in-
carnate and effective in some men—the tension of that
agony was over now. It survived not the something heal-
ing in the closeted interview with Captain Vere. Without
movement he lay as in a trance, that adolescent expression, previously noted as his, taking on something akin
to the look of a slumbering child in the cradle when the
warm hearth-glow of the still chamber of night plays on
the dimples that at whiles mysteriously form in the cheek,
silently coming and going there. For now and then in the
gyved one's trance, a serene happy light born of some wandering reminiscence or dream would diffuse itself over his
face, and then wane away only anew to return.

The chaplain coming to see him and finding him thus,
and perceiving no sign that he was conscious of his presence, attentively regarded him for a space, then slipping
aside, withdrew for the time, peradventure feeling that even
he, the minister of Christ, though receiving his stipend from
wars, had no consolation to proffer which could result in a
peace transcending that which he beheld. But in the small
hours he came again. And the prisoner, now awake to his
surroundings, noticed his approach, and civilly, all but
cheerfully, welcomed him. But it was to little purpose that
in the interview following the good man sought to bring
Billy Budd to some godly understanding that he must die,
and at dawn. True, Billy himself freely referred to his death

[handwritten annotations: "members" "drumhead" "1st Lt." "2nd Lt" "in listed man"]

as a thing close at hand; but it was something in the way that children will refer to death in general, who yet among their other sports will play a funeral with hearse and mourners. Not that like children Billy was incapable of conceiving what death really is. No, but he was wholly without irrational fear of it, a fear more prevalent in highly civilised communities than those so-called barbarous ones which in all respects stand nearer to unadulterate Nature. And, as elsewhere said, a barbarian Billy radically was; quite as much so (for all the costume) as his countrymen the British captives, living trophies made to march in the Roman triumph of Germanicus. Quite as much so as those later barbarians, young men probably, and picked specimens among the earlier British converts to Christianity, at least nominally such, and taken to Rome (as to-day converts from lesser isles of the sea may be taken to London), of whom the Pope of that time, admiring the strangeness of their personal beauty, so unlike the Italian stamp, their clear, ruddy complexions and curled flaxen locks, exclaimed, "Angels" (meaning *English,* the modern derivative), "Angels do you call them? And is it because they look so like Angels?" Had it been later in time one would think that the Pope had in mind Fra Angelico's seraphs, some of whom, plucking apples in gardens of Hesperides, have the faint rosebud complexion of the more beautiful English girls.

XXI

If in vain the good chaplain sought to impress the young barbarian with ideas of death akin to those conveyed in the skull, dial, and cross-bones on old tombstones; equally futile to all appearance were his efforts to bring home to him the thought of salvation and a Saviour. Billy listened, but less out of awe or reverence, perhaps, than from a certain natural politeness; doubtless at bottom regarding all that in much the same way that most mariners of his class take any discourse, abstract or out of the common tone of the workaday world. And this sailor way of taking clerical discourse is not wholly unlike the way in which the pioneer

of Christianity, full of transcendent miracles, was received
long ago on tropic isles by any superior *savage* so called—
a Tahitian, say, of Captain Cook's time or shortly after that
time. Out of natural courtesy he received but did not appreciate. It was like a gift placed in the palm of an outstretched hand upon which the fingers do not close.

But the *Indomitable's* chaplain was a discreet man pos-
sessing the good sense of a good heart. So he insisted not
on his vocation here. At the instance of Captain Vere, a
lieutenant had apprised him of pretty much everything as
to Billy; and since he felt that innocence was even a better
thing than religion wherewith to go to judgment, he re-
luctantly withdrew; but in his emotion not without first
performing an act strange enough in an Englishman, and
under the circumstances yet more so in any regular priest.
Stooping over, he kissed on the fair cheek his fellow-man,
a felon in martial law, one who, though in the confines of
death, he felt he could never convert to a dogma; nor for
all that did he fear for his future.

Marvel not that having been made acquainted with the
young sailor's essential innocence, the worthy man lifted
not a finger to avert the doom of such a martyr to martial
discipline. So to do would not only have been as idle as
invoking the desert, but would also have been an auda-
cious transgression of the bounds of his function, one as
exactly prescribed to him by military law as that of the
boatswain or any other naval officer. Bluntly put, a chaplain is the minister of the Prince of Peace serving in the
host of the God of War—Mars. As such, he is as incongruous as a musket would be on the altar at Christmas.
Why, then, is he there? Because he indirectly subserves
the purpose attested by the cannon; because, too, he lends
the sanction of the religion of the meek to that which practically is the abrogation of everything but force.

XXII

The night so luminous on the spar-deck (otherwise on
the cavernous ones below—levels so like the tiered gal-

leries in a coal-mine) passed away. Like the prophet in the chariot disappearing in heaven and dropping his mantle to Elisha, the withdrawing night transferred its pale robe to the peeping day. A meek, shy light appeared in the east, where stretched a diaphanous fleece of white furrowed vapour. That light slowly waxed. Suddenly *one bell* was struck aft, responded to by one louder metallic stroke from forward. It was four o'clock in the morning. Instantly the silver whistles were heard summoning all hands to witness punishment. Up through the great hatchway, rimmed with racks of heavy shot, the watch-below came pouring, overspreading with the watch already on deck the space between the mainmast and foremast, including that occupied by the capacious launch and the black booms tiered on either side of it, boat and booms making a summit of observation for the powder-boys and younger tars. A different group comprising one watch of topmen leaned over the side of the rail of that sea-balcony, no small one in a seventy-four, looking down on the crowd below. Man or boy, none spake but in whispers, and few spake at all. Captain Vere—as before, the central figure among the assembled commissioned officers—stood nigh the break of the poop-deck, facing forward. Just below him on the quarterdeck the marines in full equipment were drawn up much as at the scene of the promulgated sentence.

At sea in the old time, the execution by halter of a military sailor was generally from the fore-yard. In the present instance, for special reasons, the main-yard was assigned. Under an arm of that yard the prisoner was presently brought up, the chaplain attending him. It was noted at the time, and remarked upon afterwards, that in this final scene the good man evinced little or nothing of the perfunctory. Brief speech indeed he had with the condemned one, but the genuine Gospel was less on his tongue than in his aspect and manner toward him. The final preparations personal to the latter being speedily brought to an end by two boatswain's-mates, the consummation impended. Billy stood facing aft. At the penultimate moment, his words, his only ones, words wholly unobstructed in the utterance, were these—"God bless Cap-

tain Vere!" Syllables so unanticipated coming from one
with the ignominious hemp about his neck—a conventional
felon's benediction directed aft toward the quarters of
honour; syllables which, delivered in the clear melody of
a singing-bird on the point of launching from the twig, had
a phenomenal effect, not unenhanced by the rare personal
beauty of the young sailor, spiritualised now through late
experiences so poignantly profound.

Without volition, as it were, as if indeed the ship's popu-
lace were the vehicles of some vocal current-electric, with
one voice, from alow and aloft, came a resonant echo—
"God bless Captain Vere!" And yet at that instant Billy
alone must have been in their hearts, even as he was in
their eyes.

At the pronounced words and the spontaneous echo
that voluminously resounded them, Captain Vere, either
through stoic self-control or a sort of momentary paralysis induced by emotional shock, stood erectly rigid as a
musket in the ship-armourer's rack.

The hull, deliberately recovering from the periodic roll
to the leeward, was just regaining an even keel, when the
last signal, the preconcerted dumb one, was given. At the
same moment it chanced that the vapoury fleece hanging
low in the east was shot through with a soft glory as of
the fleece of the Lamb of God seen in mystical vision, and
simultaneously therewith, watched by the wedged mass of
upturned faces, Billy ascended; and ascending, took the
full rose of the dawn.

In the pinioned figure, arrived at the yard-end, to the
wonder of all, no motion was apparent save that created
by the slow roll of the hull, in moderate weather so ma-
jestic in a great ship heavy-cannoned.

A Digression

When some days afterwards in reference to the singularity just mentioned, the purser, a rather ruddy, rotund
person, more accurate as an accountant than profound as
a philosopher, said at mess to the surgeon, "What testi-

mony to the force lodged in the will-power," the latter, spare and tall, one in whom a discreet causticity went along with a manner less genial than polite, replied, "Your pardon, Mr. Purser. In a hanging scientifically conducted— and under special orders I myself directed how Budd's was to be effected—any movement following the completed suspension and originating in the body suspended, such movement indicates mechanical spasm in the muscular system. Hence the absence of that is no more attributable to will-power, as you call it, than to horse-power—begging your pardon."

"But this muscular spasm you speak of, is not that in a degree more or less invariable in these cases?"

"Assuredly so, Mr. Purser."

"How then, my good sir, do you account for its absence in this instance?"

"Mr. Purser, it is clear that your sense of the singularity in this matter equals not mine. You account for it by what you call will-power, a term not yet included in the lexicon of science. For me I do not with my present knowledge pretend to account for it at all. Even should one assume the hypothesis that at the first touch of the halyards the action of Budd's heart, intensified by extraordinary emotion at its climax, abruptly stopped—much like a watch when in carelessly winding it up you strain at the finish, thus snapping the chain—even under that hypothesis how account for the phenomenon that followed?"

"You admit, then, that the absence of spasmodic movement was phenomenal?"

"It was phenomenal, Mr. Purser, in the sense that it was an appearance, the cause of which is not immediately to be assigned."

"But tell me, my dear sir," pertinaciously continued the other, "was the man's death effected by the halter, or was it a species of euthanasia?"

"*Euthanasia,* Mr. Purser, is something like your willpower; I doubt its authenticity as a scientific term—begging your pardon again. It is at once imaginative and metaphysical—in short, Greek. But," abruptly changing his

[handwritten margin notes:]
power?

phenomenal Death. leads to supernatural

money on ship.

Quotes?

→ takes care of

old meaning - painless death
new meaning - mercy killing

tone, "there is a case in the sick-bay that I do not care to leave to my assistants. Beg your pardon, but excuse me." And rising from the mess he formally withdrew.

XXIII

The silence at the moment of execution, and for a moment or two continuing thereafter, but emphasised by the regular wash of the sea against the hull, or the flutter of a sail caused by the helmsman's eyes being tempted astray, this emphasised silence was gradually disturbed by a sound not easily to be verbally rendered. Whoever has heard the freshet-wave of a torrent suddenly swelled by pouring showers in tropical mountains, showers not shared by the plain; whoever has heard the first muffled murmur of its sloping advance through precipitous woods, may form some conception of the sound now heard. The seeming remoteness of its source was because of its murmurous indistinctness, since it came from close by, even from the men massed on the ship's open deck. Being inarticulate, it was dubious in significance further than it seemed to indicate some capricious revulsion of thought or feeling such as mobs ashore are liable to, in the present instance possibly implying a sullen revocation on the men's part of their involuntary echoing of Billy's benediction. But ere the murmur had time to wax into clamour it was met by a strategic command, the more telling that it came with abrupt unexpectedness.

"Pipe down the starboard watch, boatswain, and see that they go."

Shrill as the shriek of the sea-hawk the whistles of the boatswain and his mates pierced that ominous low sound dissipating it; and yielding to the mechanism of discipline the throng was thinned by one half. For the remainder, most of them were set to temporary employments connected with trimming the yards and so forth, business readily to be found upon occasion by an officer-of-the-deck.

Now each proceeding that follows a mortal sentence pronounced at sea by a drum-head court is characterised by promptitude not perceptibly merging into hurry, though bordering that. The hammock, the one which had been Billy's bed when alive, having already been ballasted with shot, and otherwise prepared to serve for his canvas coffin, the last office of the sea-undertakers, the sailmaker's mates, was now speedily completed. When everything was in readiness a second call for all hands, made necessary by the strategic movement before mentioned, was sounded, and now to witness burial.

The details of this closing formality it needs not to give. But when the tilted plank let slide its freight into the sea, a second strange human murmur was heard, blended now with another inarticulate sound proceeding from certain larger sea-fowl, who, their attention having been attracted by the peculiar commotion in the water resulting from the heavy sloped dive of the shotted hammock into the sea, flew screaming to the spot. So near the hull did they come, that the stridor or bony creak of their gaunt double-jointed pinions was audible. As the ship under light airs passed on, leaving the burial spot astern, they still kept circling it low down with the moving shadow of their outstretched wings and the croaked requiem of their cries.

Upon sailors as superstitious as those of the age preceding ours, man-of-war's men, too, who had just beheld the prodigy of repose in the form suspended in air and now floundering in the deeps; to such mariners the action of the sea-fowl, though dictated by mere animal greed for prey, was big with no prosaic significance. An uncertain movement began among them, in which some encroachment was made. It was tolerated but for a moment. For suddenly the drum beat to quarters, which familiar sound happening at least twice every day, had upon the present occasion a signal peremptoriness in it. True martial discipline long continued superinduces in average man a sort of impulse of docility whose operation at the official tone of command much resembles in its promptitude the effect of an instinct.

The drum-beat dissolved the multitude, distributing most of them along the batteries of the two covered gun-decks. There, as wont, the gun crews stood by their respective cannon erect and silent. In due course the first officer, sword under arm and standing in his place on the quarter-deck, formally received the successive reports of the sworded lieutenants commanding the sections of batteries below; the last of which reports being made, the summed report he delivered with the customary salute to the commander. All this occupied time, which in the present case was the object of beating to quarters at an hour prior to the customary one. That such variance from usage was authorised by an officer like Captain Vere, a martinet as some deemed him, was evidence of the necessity for unusual action implied in what he deemed to be temporarily the mood of his men. "With mankind," he would say, "forms, measured forms, are everything; and that is the import couched in the story of Orpheus with his lyre spell-binding the wild denizens of the woods." And this he once applied to the disruption of forms going on across the Channel and the consequences thereof.

At this unwonted muster at quarters all proceeded as at the regular hour. The band on the quarter-deck played a sacred air. After which the chaplain went through the customary morning service. That done, the drum beat the retreat, and toned by music and religious rites subserving the discipline and purpose of war, the men in their wonted orderly manner dispersed to the places allotted them when not at the guns.

And now it was full day. The fleece of low-hanging vapour had vanished, licked up by the sun that late had so glorified it. And the circumambient air in the clearness of its serenity was like smooth white marble in the polished block not yet removed from the marble-dealer's yard.

XXIV

The symmetry of form attainable in pure fiction cannot so readily be achieved in a narration essentially having less to do with fable than with fact. Truth uncompromisingly told will always have its ragged edges; hence the conclusion

of such a narration is apt to be less finished than an archi-
tectural finial.

How it fared with the Handsome Sailor during the year
of the Great Mutiny has been faithfully given. But though
properly the story ends with his life, something in way of
sequel will not be amiss. Three brief chapters will suffice.

In the general re-christening under the Directory of the
craft originally forming the navy of the French Monarchy,
the *St. Louis* line-of-battle ship was named the *Athéiste.*
Such a name, like some other substituted ones in the Revolutionary fleet, while proclaiming the infidel audacity of the
ruling power, was yet, though not so intended to be, the
aptest name, if one consider it, ever given to a warship;
far more so indeed than the *Devastation,* the *Erebus* (the
Hell), and similar names bestowed upon fighting-ships.

On the return passage to the English fleet from the detached cruise during which occurred the events already
recorded, the *Indomitable* fell in with the *Athéiste.* An
engagement ensued, during which Captain Vere, in the
act of putting his ship alongside the enemy with a view of
throwing his boarders across the bulwarks, was hit by a
musket-ball from a port-hole of the enemy's main cabin.
More than disabled, he dropped to the deck and was carried below to the same cock-pit where some of his men
already lay. The senior lieutenant took command. Under
him the enemy was finally captured, and though much
crippled, was by rare good fortune successfully taken into
Gibraltar, an English port not very distant from the scene
of the fight. There Captain Vere with the rest of the
wounded was put ashore. He lingered for some days, but
the end came. Unhappily he was cut off too early for the
Nile and Trafalgar. The spirit that despite its philosophic
austerity may yet have indulged in the most secret of all
passions, ambition, never attained to the fulness of fame.

Not long before death, while lying under the influence
of that magical drug which, soothing the physical frame,
mysteriously operates on the subtler element in man, he
was heard to murmur words inexplicable to his attendant
—"Billy Budd, Billy Budd." That these were not the ac-
cents of remorse, would seem clear from what the at-

tendant said to the *Indomitable's* senior officer of marines, who, as the most reluctant to condemn of the members of the drum-head court, too well knew, though here he kept the knowledge to himself, who Billy Budd was.

XXV

Some few weeks after the execution, among other matters under the head of *News from the Mediterranean,* there appeared in a naval chronicle of the time, an authorised weekly publication, an account of the affair. It was doubtless for the most part written in good faith, though the medium, partly rumour, through which the facts must have reached the writer, served to deflect, and in part falsify them. Because it appeared in a publication now long ago superannuated and forgotten, and is all that hitherto has stood in human record to attest what manner of men respectively were John Claggart and Billy Budd, it is here reproduced.

"On the tenth of the last month a deplorable occurrence took place on board H.M.S. *Indomitable.* John Claggart, the ship's master-at-arms, discovering that some sort of plot was incipient among an inferior section of the ship's company, and that the ringleader was one William Budd, he, Claggart, in the act of arraigning the man before the captain was vindictively stabbed to the heart by the suddenly drawn sheath-knife of Budd.

"The deed and the implement employed sufficiently suggest that though mustered into the service under an English name the assassin was no Englishman, but one of those aliens adopting an English cognomen whom the present extraordinary necessities of the Service have caused to be admitted into it in considerable numbers.

"The enormity of the crime and the extreme depravity of the criminal, appear the greater in view of the character of the victim, a middle-aged man, respectable and discreet, belonging to that minor official grade, the petty officers, upon whom, as none know better than the commis-

sioned gentlemen, the efficiency of His Majesty's Navy so
largely depends. His function was a responsible one; at
once onerous and thankless, and his fidelity in it the
greater because of his strong patriotic impulse. In this
instance, as in so many other instances in these days, the
character of the unfortunate man signally refutes, if refu-
tation were needed, that peevish saying attributed to Dr.
Johnson that patriotism is the last refuge of a scoundrel.

"The criminal paid the penalty of his crime. The promptitude of the punishment has proved salutary. Nothing
amiss is now apprehended aboard H.M.S. *Indomitable*."

ironical —

XXVI

Everything is for a season remarkable in navies. Any
tangible object associated with some striking incident of
the service is converted into a monument. The spar from
which the foretopman was suspended was for some few
years kept trace of by the blue-jackets. Then knowledge
followed it from ship to dockyard and again from dock-
yard to ship, still pursuing it even when at last reduced to
a mere dockyard boom. To them a chip of it was as a piece
of the Cross. Ignorant though they were of the real facts
of the happening and not thinking but that the penalty was
unavoidably inflicted from the naval point of view, for all
that they instinctively felt that Billy was a sort of man as
incapable of mutiny as of wilful murder. They recalled the
fresh young image of the Handsome Sailor, that face never
deformed by a sneer or subtler vile freak of the heart within! This impression of him was doubtless deepened by the
fact that he was gone and in a measure mysteriously gone.
On the gun-decks of the *Indomitable* the general estimate
of his nature and its unconscious simplicity eventually
found rude utterance from another foretopman, one of his
own watch, gifted as some sailors are, with an artless poetic
temperament. The tarry hands made some lines, which,
after circulating among the shipboard crew for a while,
finally got rudely printed at Portsmouth as a ballad. The
title given to it was the sailor's.

Moral - society avoids Individuals
rights + follows rules for the
sake of rules.

BILLY IN THE DARBIES

Good of the Chaplain to enter Lone Bay
And down on his marrow-bones here and pray.
For the likes just o' me, Billy Budd.—But look:
Through the port comes the moon-shine astray!
It tips the guard's cutlass and silvers this nook;
But 'twill die in the dawning of Billy's last day.
A jewel-block they'll make of me to-morrow,
Pendant pearl from the yard-arm-end
Like the ear-drop I gave to Bristol Molly—
Oh, 'tis me, not the sentence, they'll suspend.
Ay, ay, all is up; and I must up too
Early in the morning, aloft from alow.
On an empty stomach, now, never it would do.
They'll give me a nibble—bit o' biscuit ere I go.
Sure, a messmate will reach me the last parting cup;
But turning heads away from the hoist and the belay,
Heaven knows who will have the running of me up!
No pipe to those halyards—but aren't it all sham?
A blur's in my eyes; it is dreaming that I am,
A hatchet to my panzer? all adrift to go?
The drum roll to grog, and Billy never know?
But Donald he has promised to stand by the plank;
So I'll shake a friendly hand ere I sink.
But—no! It is dead then I'll be, come to think.
I remember Taff the Welshman when he sank.
And his cheek it was like the budding pink.
But me, they'll lash me in hammock, drop me deep
Fathoms down, fathoms down, how I'll dream fast
    asleep.
I feel it stealing now. Sentry, are you there?
Just ease these darbies at the wrist,
And roll me over fair.
I am sleepy, and the oozy weeds about me twist.

END OF BOOK,
April 19, 1891.

[Handwritten annotations:]

Billy
(innocence)

Captain Vere
(prudence)
elf control
Marshel law.

Claggant
(natural
depravity
innate
evil.

PART TWO

Clues to Understanding the Mysteries in *Billy Budd*

A student's life is not a happy one. He cannot sit down and just read a book; he has to go back over it and read it again, trying to find out what it means.

Naturally, this seems to be the fault of teachers and critics who insist that a book never means what it says, or that it means so much MORE than it says that the reader must dig and dig, and dig some more, to make doubly sure he hasn't missed anything important.

INNERMEANINGITIS

The result is that everybody contracts what one boy called "a bad case of innermeaningitis." A reader may well ask: "Do authors really mean all those things? And if they do, why don't they say so!" If the dissection continues, it is not long before another cry is heard: "All this analysis . . . it's ruining the book!"

This perilous pit is very near for anyone approaching Herman Melville's *Billy Budd*. Here is a book that obviously does not say all it means, and for which the author left no convenient study guides. It can easily draw from the teacher or critic a torrent of words that may swamp both the book and any new reader. By staying on the path, however, it is possible to track down some clues to clear the mysteries.

First, two perfectly direct answers may be given to the perennial question about an author's intentions: many writers certainly do mean those inner "things" that teachers unearth. They have said so directly, as in the case of Shirley Jackson's famous symbolic tale "The Lottery." On the other hand, as many teachers will admit, they sometimes go too far, and too deep. Robert Frost could be quite satirical about some of the interpretations that professors made of his poetry when they were carried away.

For a reader, however, there is something more important than whether a certain writer did intend those "inner meanings." It is whether the meanings are logical, natural, and correct in relation to all the rest of the book. If they are, they are perfectly justified, even if new to the author. Some authors in fact have said, "No, I didn't really think of that, but maybe I should have." Or . . . "That's a perfectly natural result of what I did intend." Then, there is the record of a conversation between Melville and Mrs. Nathaniel Hawthorne in which he admitted that she made him see the real significance of one part of *Moby Dick*. And there is no question that the most joyful, intelligent, and profitable readers are those who bring to the books they study all they know of other books, actual experience, and their own world of imagination.

All these ideas about reading are pertinent to *Billy Budd*, for the book is written in a strange pattern, one that inevitably excites imaginative, contradictory, and elaborate interpretations. By the word "pattern," I mean arrangement of chapters, inclusion and exclusion of material, choice of a particular narrator, references to books, famous men, and history, and what Melville admitted were "digressions."

All of these structural matters, plus the peculiar mood of the language, conspire to puzzle the reader, for at times they actually get in the way of what the reader wants to know. It seems, in fact, as if there is a direct conflict between Melville's method and the kind of story he was telling. The trouble is that, with a swift, emotional, and dramatic story in mind, Melville chose to write in a slow, reasonable, and undramatic fashion that sounds more like an essay than a novel.

THE STORY

The story begins when Billy, a young and innocent sailor, is forced into service on a British warship, the *Indomitable*.

It is 1797, a time of violence, for the French nation has just been torn apart by the great Revolution, and the British navy has been shocked by two violent mutinies. Billy's ship, commanded by a quiet but firm Captain, Edward Vere, puts to sea in an atmosphere of distrust, mutiny, and war. Without any justifiable reason whatever, the ship's police officer, John Claggart, becomes suspicious of Billy and falsely charges him with mutinous feelings against Captain Vere. Billy, who is inarticulate, protests his innocence in a fit of temper and kills Claggart in front of the captain. A summary court-martial condemns Billy to death, and he is executed before the entire ship's crew, with no explanation of the truth by Captain Vere. Later Vere is killed in action. Subsequently the only public statement of the case is contained in an official Navy publication, which completely upholds Claggart and his Captain. In telling the story, Melville writes from the point of view of a narrator who has discovered part of the truth.

One peculiarity of the method is that for the first thirty pages, about half the story, almost nothing happens. Melville fills the space with character analysis, speculation, essay writing, digressions, historical allusions, and tiny bits of dialogue. Then, suddenly, the action erupts, so swiftly that the reader hardly has time to notice the details. It is followed by a leisurely narrative of the investigation, trial, and execution, and the book ends with several chapters of abstract commentary, remarks by extraneous characters, and, on the last page, a very sentimental ballad. Nowhere are there breathless accounts of men against men, and men against the sea, nor is there any love interest.

What was Melville up to? Didn't he know what kind of story he had invented? Why didn't he write it like his other books—full of dialogue, action, and blood? Why didn't he compose an exciting play, as two contemporary authors have done? . . . or find someone to collaborate with him on an opera, as three English artists have done? Anyone who has read *Mutiny on the Bounty* or *The Caine Mutiny* can see what he MIGHT have done.

BOUNTY OF ALLUSIONS

Why is the story filled with allusions to other books, to
the founder of Christianity, to famous war heroes, to great
events in history, and to criminals, businessmen, animals,
and barbarians? The list is impressive: The Bible, Jesus
Christ, Captain Horatio Nelson, the French Revolution,
the Nore and Spithead mutinies, horses, heifers, night-
ingales, and Germanicus. Instead of a direct start, Melville
opens with a long comparison of Billy Budd and a Negro
sailor who has nothing whatever to do with the story.
Most curious, too, is the inclusion of ideas pertinent to
modern psychiatry; and, in an emphatic position at the
end, the controversial idea of euthanasia is introduced by
a minor character who plays no part in the tale.

BAFFLING OMISSIONS

Why does Melville tell the story through a narrator,
clearly referred to as "I" and "me," as if he were an actual
person, and yet never reveal his identity? Other writers
have named their narrators, given them individual personalities, and made it clear why they would tell their stories.
Most baffling of all, perhaps, is the question: Where did
this unknown narrator find his material? Much of it was
unknown or incomprehensible to the characters, and the
only available source referred to is the official "release,"
a complete package of lies. This is just one aspect of the
conspiracy of silence and ignorance that infects the whole
story.

There is the bald fact, for example, that the reader is
told almost nothing about the lives of two of the main
characters: Billy, and his destroyer, the master-at-arms,
John Claggart. Melville does give a few details of Captain
Vere's life, but even here, particularly at the end, the man
is shrouded in ambiguous references. And on nearly every
page, some act or expression is described "which no one
observed," or some element of character is mentioned as
being beyond common understanding. The climax comes

after the story is over, when the reader realizes that the three main characters, who knew more than anyone else, are dead, and the three who had some inkling of the truth are so submissive that they would never say a word. These are the members of the court that "convicted" Billy.

Finally, there is one of the most puzzling problems in the plan of the entire story: Why did Melville not tell the most fascinating scene of all—the interview between Billy and the Captain, in which the latter had to tell Billy that he had been condemned. This is a scene crying to be written, since it involves a spectacular conflict between two men who knew that although Billy was morally innocent, and Claggart was an evil liar, Billy must be crucified. What the reader is given instead is a soft official guess, in the phony language of a government publicity hand-out. There are other dramatic omissions, too, such as the complete speech Captain Vere made to the crew "explaining" what happened in his cabin, and a description of Claggart's true feelings about the horrid lies he told about Billy.

WHAT!—an inquisitive and exasperated student will ask—is the point? Do these contradictions and ambiguities suggest anything about Melville's intentions?

THE ISSUES

First of all, it can be definitely said that some of the author's purposes are absolutely clear. The opening page is intended to make the reader think, not only because Melville talks directly about "thinkers," but because the issues raised are thoughtful ones—large, basic, and moral —rather than active, or pertaining to individual characters. Two of the most compelling issues are Right against Wrong, and Mutiny against Authority. This attention to moral conflict continues throughout the story, for even after the characters have been given some degree of individuality, they are constantly related to comprehensive, abstract principles: Billy to "innocence," Captain Vere to "prudence," and the ship's police officer, Claggart, to "natural depravity."

Furthermore, Melville, in a steadily increasing attack,

intended to shock the reader into a fearful consciousness of the contradiction between appearance and reality. He not only mentions this issue in generalizations like "War looks but to the frontage, the appearance," but dramatizes it in the specific fact that to Billy, Claggart appears friendly and respectable, whereas the reader already knows just how fiercely the master-at-arms envies and hates the young sailor. Then, at the climax, with the reader knowing virtually all of the "inside story," Melville invents an official Navy "whitewash," which spells out in black and white the ironic difference between truth and "keeping up appearances."

THE MAIN EFFECTS

Still, however, there are all those contradictions and peculiarities of method. The final section of this investigation will show that they produce effects in the reader's mind that are logical, natural, and appropriate to the story as a whole, even though Melville did not say he intended them. I am going to describe some of these main effects with the idea that any reader may take them or leave them, but if he takes them he may find "clear" hints as to the writer's dark purposes. Or, to add a slightly different emphasis, what I will be describing is one method of reading a book, a method that is a direct result of the method of writing that book.

The contradictions between method and story, like the opposing forces in electricity, can produce a current of thinking that resolves the conflict. The long psychological analysis of Claggart, for example, which seems to slow the book to a stumble, turns out to be absolutely necessary, since it reveals the only acceptable reason why he hated Billy and denounced him to the Captain. The story is totally unbelievable without this profound spying on the "inside narrative" of Claggart's emotions. The master-at-arms, with his natural depravity, envied "the good looks, cheery health and frank enjoyment of young life in Billy, because these went along with a nature that as Claggart magnetically felt, had in its simplicity never willed malice or experienced the reactionary bite of that serpent." This is part of Melville's explanation of that mysterious antagonism that arises in certain "exceptional mortals by the mere aspect of some other mortal"—especially if the other is better looking. It is quite natural for the reader to turn this into modern language, and think of people who are vengeful "just because I can't stand the sight of that character!"

Such reading by association is quite natural to the whole book, particularly in connection with Melville's ambiguous and seemingly disjointed style: it almost forces the reader to find relationships within the digressions of the story. In a straight narrative, which sweeps the reader along on dramatic waves, no such intellectual juggling is needed. In *Billy Budd* it is inevitable, and full of surprises. The reader who allows his mental habits to be sharpened by Melville's provoking patterns may remember, at the climax, the earlier passage about Captain Nelson; if so, Captain Vere's actions are clarified by the contrast. A reader adept at associating with the right places may recall, too, that Captain Vere was first described as "modest," "intellectual," and "disinterested," creating an impression of a man impervious to outside pressure. Yet at the end he acts so strangely that others think he may be "unhinged"; he prejudges Billy to hang, forces the court to condemn him, and rigidly suppresses the truth. These contradictions make the reader wonder whether Vere acted out of thoughtful, unselfish reasons—as he claimed—or plain fear of his crew and of loss of reputation. Such a conclusion would be logically consistent with Melville's great emphasis on the conflict between reality and appearance. It is also closely associated with the fact that there is so little action that it seems as though Melville deliberately kept the book quiet to clear the air for moral and philosophical conclusions.

The reader also feels that instead of following a straight story, he is watching a steady piling up of all kinds of forces, ideas, causes, and images which, though isolated when they appear, eventually crowd together on the *Indomitable* and collide to make the climax. Melville is like a master scientist experimenting with a great variety of ingredients to see what will happen when they are poured into one bottle.

This effect is intensified by the rich parade of allusions that appear around the corner of every page. The reader cannot escape thinking of Billy in relation to Christ or Adam, Captain Vere to Horatio Nelson, the general situation to the French Revolution, Billy's conviction to a similar affair on an American man-of-war, and the conduct of his trial to normal court procedures. But the method of analogy goes further: it suggests comparisons outside the book, within the reader's experience. Billy's punishment, based solely on his one action, is a reminder of two opposed systems of justice that are still being debated, particularly among parents, students, and teachers —that which considers nothing but the broken rule, and that which says the reasons for the transgression must be taken into account. Such an analogy can carry the reader along—or away—into many extra meanings, if he is willing.

I have already mentioned the mood of the language, as well as the method of narrative, as a source of puzzlement for the reader. By this I mean the repetition of words like "secrecy," "unknown," "mystery," "rumor," "indirection," and "ignorance"; the construction of sentences in which one part seems to contradict another; plus the specific statement that certain elements in the story the reader "must determine for himself by such light as this narrative may afford." With all this murky "atmosphere," the reader is likely to end the book in suspended animation, particularly when he realizes that Melville never identifies his narrator.

Usually, I have a nasty scorn for the idea that a book must have a "moral" to be good; but there are exceptions, and in the case of *Billy Budd,* I am quite convinced that one of the dominating themes is IGNORANCE. I find it everywhere: in words, facts, allusions, "inner meanings," and the characters' lives. It is a strange book, unlike any other I know, in that almost nobody knows anything about anybody else, and if the reader imagines the story as a report on actual life, as Melville intended, he looks back on it as very like some of the great mysteries of man's existence—like the total disappearance of ships, and the assassination of President Kennedy. It is almost as if Melville wrote the book to plague the reader with his ignorance, to make him feel like Billy, who didn't know where he was born or who his father was.

Like *Hamlet, Billy Budd* is a book to torment and inspire the reader's imagination. It is a fascinating and mysterious and a creative experience to read the book slowly. Consider the final point: the omission of scenes that might have been written—like Captain Vere's speech to the crew, and the interview between the Captain and Billy behind closed doors.

Great and provoking questions arise here: Would the crew have been incapable of understanding, as some teachers have said about students when it was proposed that the facts of a discipline case be explained? Wouldn't the crew perhaps have had MORE respect for Captain Vere because he spoke out, refusing to take the conventional and easy approach? Wouldn't the truth have lessened the possibility of mutiny?

One of the main effects of the omissions I have discussed is that the book is in a sense not a regular work of fiction at all, but a work of art so close to life that it is more life than art. Here, for a change, the author is on the reader's side. Melville, himself, wrote in the novel that the "symmetry of form attainable in pure fiction can not so readily be achieved in a narration essentially having less to do with fable than with fact. Truth uncompromisingly told will always have its ragged edges. . . ."

Billy Budd dramatizes a special kind of reading: one that asks the reader to fill in—as life does. This kind of reading is difficult in America because we do so love to "lay it on the line"; but it is a far more interesting way to live than merely reading words once over lightly. Also, a student must assume that books, like women, mean more than they say, and pursue that meaning like skin-divers after sunken treasure.

PART THREE

A Man vs. the Rules:
Sources and Environment

FORCE OF RULES IN THE 19TH CENTURY

In the 19th century, before the spirit of research and demonstration infected the world, man, when he was challenged, did not worry much about whether he was right or wrong: he knew perfectly well that no one could PROVE him wrong, so he simply pointed to the old rules with a violent finger and yelled louder than his opponent, "I am RIGHT—you are WRONG—Q.E.D.—Per Order!"

Or, like Captain Vere when the sailors began to mutter suspiciously about Billy Budd's execution, he jammed his authority down their throats with ritual noises. The Captain ordered a swift, belligerent drum-roll to beat the men back to quarters. His justification? "With mankind, forms, measured forms are everything."

With this blinding weapon all manner of men protected themselves in authority: Captains, Governors, Schoolmasters, Censors, and Fathers. They were secure in the knowledge that even if they suffered from personal doubts— which very few did—there was no real opposition, physical, intellectual, or spiritual as long as they *followed the rules*.

Some scholars argue that it is inappropriate to speak of Melville as a "rebel," and certainly he did not write as angrily as the "angry young men" of modern England; but a close test of *Billy Budd,* matching the book with some of its most obvious sources, will show that without any question the author was emotionally and intellectually concerned with the battle between man and the rules of authority. At the end he does not provide an absolute standard of right and wrong—perhaps because Science had not invented the tools of proof—but he does provoke questions and suggest answers that would have made men in authority angry if the book had been published when it was written, in 1891.

Melville had already caused trouble by revealing, in his early books about the South Pacific, that the powerful American missionaries were autocratic and cruel, and had been warned that he had better not suggest such evil ideas again. In later books he turned his research to other despots, and this time he could not be stopped, for he had seen these little Hitlers in actual practice on board ship, and on several occasions had almost suffered himself from their bitter belligerence. Also, he remembered particularly the victim's innocence, or his mere breaking of tiny regulations, topped by the pathetic irony of vicious punishment far out of proportion to the "crime."

In Melville's time, authority appeared to be interested only in appearances, not only in combat—"War looks but to the frontage, the appearance," rationalized Captain Vere —but in peace. The 19th century produced one long show —of manners, clothes, elaborate houses, and public affectation of high feeling. Since Melville lived in the Berkshires, he must have seen the first flood of rich industrial monsters who swamped the region and left behind gross palaces of bad taste.

Another great fact of the 19th century, which was treated much more directly in *Billy Budd,* was the total lack of interest in motives, or reasons for behavior, so that when rules were broken the only thing considered was the act and its consequences. No exceptions were allowed. Captain Vere sums up this old philosophy with a sharp tongue when one of Billy's judges objects: "But surely Budd purposed neither mutiny nor homicide."

"Surely not, my good man . . . but we proceed under the law of the Mutiny Act. . . . Budd's intent or non-intent is nothing to the purpose."

Thus was Justice done, and the sanctity of rules preserved, as in a bottle.

Against the whirlwind of these authoritarian ideas, Melville stood out, detached, in the manner of a scientific observer and an independent philosopher. The climax of his attitude was the novel *Billy Budd,* which resulted from the collision of Melville's own skeptical nature with actual human experience—his own while serving as a professional sailor, and his eventual discovery of two sensational cases of mutiny, the "Somers" affair in the U. S. Navy and the "Spithead" mutiny in England.

MELVILLE'S NAVY EXPERIENCES

In the following passage from his biography of Melville, Leon Howard traces some of the relationships between the author's struggles on shipboard and the development of his novel about man against the rules:

To create his hypothetical "inside narrative" Melville, at first, drew heavily upon his own experiences in the Navy as he had transmuted them into *White Jacket.* He attributed to his hero, Billy, his own horror at the practice of flogging, his own meticulous efforts to avoid so much as a reprimand, and his own imagined desperation at the prospect of unjust punishment. He also gave a prominent place in his story to the two great sources of mental disturbance he found in his period of service: a vicious master-at-arms who had the unassailable power of a privileged informer, and the perpetual threat of the severe articles of war under which the ship was ruled. These, in fact, provided him with his solution to the puzzle he had undertaken to solve. Drawing freely upon his memory of John C. Turner of the *United States* as he had represented him as the character "Bland" in *White Jacket,* he made the master-at-arms a major character in his story—a sort of Iago, villainous by nature and driven to the practice of his particular dark design by envy of the handsome appearance and frank nature of Billy Budd. John Claggart, as he was called in the tale, was represented as falsely accusing Billy of fomenting mutiny; and Billy, feeling the desperation Melville had once imagined he might feel under some such circumstances, struck him dead in his spasmodic inability to answer the accusation. Captain Vere, although fully aware of the situation, was caught between the overt act he had witnessed and the discipline required by the articles of war he was sworn to enforce. He was obliged to compel the court-martial to sentence Billy to death. And Billy, dumbly aware of the good will and even love which existed beneath the surface of the captain's necessity, was hanged with the exclamation "God bless Captain Vere!" on his lips.

THE SOMERS AFFAIR

If Melville had based his novel only on his own experiences, he might have written *Billy Budd* as the straight story Mr. Howard has retold. But before the book was finished, Melville had to wrestle with his knowledge of the two naval tragedies already mentioned. In another part of his biography Mr. Howard describes the "Somers" affair, and Melville's dramatic relation to it. As the writer was returning home from the South Pacific, he began to hear from sailors in the American Navy:

. . . a story which affected his meditations upon the articles of war and was to be introduced into his later account of his naval experiences and stay in his mind as long as he lived. Over a year before, a mysterious "mutiny" had occurred on board the U. S. S. "Somers," and a midshipman named Philip Spencer, a boatswain's mate named Samuel Cromwell, and a seaman named Elisha Small had been hanged. The affair had been kept quiet until the ship reached New York in December, 1842, but had soon afterward been given wide publicity because of the mysterious circumstances surrounding the affair and because Spencer was the son of Secretary of War John C. Spencer. Almost as interesting, to the sailors of the fleet, was the report that Small (who was a great favorite with the crew) had been run up to the yardarm with the patriotic exclamation "God bless the flag!" on his lips—although a later tradition was to attribute the exclamation to Spencer and revise its wording into a tribute to his Greek-letter fraternity, Chi Psi. The secret knowledge which turned a distressing story into an obsession with Melville, however, was the fact that the Lieutenant Gansevoort who had been in charge of the court-martial was his own first cousin Guert. He could not believe that the young naval officer who had so impressed him as a boy had become the villain that he evidently appeared to be in the eyes of the common sailors of the fleet, and the puzzle doubtless bothered him through many lonely hours of his night watches and contributed to the growth of that analytic and critical attitude with which he had already begun to contemplate organized society.

After the court-martial, according to Howard's account, Melville's cousin became a man of mystery who looked the part.

. . . when the *Somers* had reached New York after its mutiny, he slipped into the home of his widowed mother looking as haggard and broken as "an infirm man of seventy." . . . While on his way to Washington shortly afterward he had stopped overnight in Philadelphia and had confided in a cousin, Passed Midshipman Henry or "Hunn" Gansevoort, that he had practically compelled a reluctant court-martial to render a sentence of "guilty" against Philip Spencer and his associates at the insistence of Captain Mackenzie, who had told him that the court had "misapprehended the aggravated character of the offense, and that there would be no security for the lives of officers or protection to commerce if an example was not made in a case so flagrant as this." The family knew nothing of this confidence, for two days later Henry had put to sea on the *Grampus,* which had been lost with all hands in March; but Guert had assured his mother that he had done his duty and that his action "was *approved* of God," however mysterious it might appear to his fellow men, and the entire family was convinced from his words and his character that he was an innocent victim of circumstances. The formal inquiry had cleared him of legal blame but had not fully resolved the mystery of the circumstances, and the matter was a distressing puzzle to all his relatives and friends who were in a position to observe its devastating and lasting effect upon him.

During Melville's lifetime there were four published discussions of the "Somers" affair that created an unhappy, dramatic atmosphere around the author while he was writing *Billy Budd:* the Navy's official condemnation of the sailors and exoneration of its officers; James Fenimore Cooper's long pamphlet in 1844, "The Cruise of the Somers," refuting this Navy attitude; and two magazine "inside stories" that also contradicted the Navy. One of these, in the June 1889 issue of *Cosmopolitan,* was entitled "The Murder of Philip Spencer."

In Cooper's piece there are several passages appropriate to the purposes of this edition of *Billy Budd,* since they give an inquisitive modern reader some idea of what Melville used, left out, and altered to suit his own purposes.

The outward passage of the "Somers" was marked by some features at which it is necessary to glance. There was in the first place, a very remarkable amount of *flogging* on board. The cat and the colt were in constant use among this sea-sick, home-sick, crew of boys. There was, to say the least, a determination to try what the lash would do, in the way of discipline. Speech-making, too, on the part of the commander, seems to have been another moral instrumentality.

Concurrently with this severity, there was a most extraordinary and inexcusable laxity of discipline in other quarters. Men were allowed to curse the commander, in the hearing of officers; to threaten to throw him overboard; and no report of it reached the commander, no record of it was made on the log-book. Indeed, if we may believe the testimony before the court-martial, the discipline fell off most alarmingly after the vessel left Madeira, and continued almost till the day in which the alleged conspiracy was divulged to the commander— a period of say, fifty days; and yet the commander was entirely unaware of the fact! INDEED, THIS VERY FALLING OFF OF THE DISCIPLINE, IS THE GRAVE CONSIDERATION WHICH THE COMMANDER AND HIS OFFICERS URGE AS CORROBORATIVE OF THE CONSPIRACY THEY FEARED, AND FOR WHICH THEY EXECUTED THREE OF THE SUBSEQUENTLY SUSPECTED PERSONS.

Two other brief passages from Cooper's work are relevant:

It is a little remarkable, that not the shadow of proof has ever been produced to show, that the commander made any PERSONAL inquiry into these matters (accusations of mutiny) before the arrest, except through the first lieutenant (Melville's cousin, who presided at the trial).

An astounding fact meets us at the threshold of this trial! In defiance of every consideration of justice, and the clearest, most indubitable of rights, THE ACCUSED WERE NOT ALLOWED THE PRIVILEGE OF APPEARING BEFORE THE COUNCIL! . . . There is not a court that would dare to make this mockery of justice; and the fact, that public execration does not follow the wardroom council of the "Somers" is because the public does not distinctly perceive the true state of things. . . .

Based on descriptions of the "Somers" affair in Cooper's pamphlet, Edmund Fuller's book called *Mutiny,* and official Navy statements, there are three other interesting points of comparison and contrast which gives some idea of how Melville treated his source materials in writing *Billy Budd.*

1. In both cases, despite strong doubts, the two captains acted summarily upon charges of mutiny exactly as reported by their subordinates, Lieutenant Gansevoort and master-at-arms Claggart.

2. Whereas Commander Mackenzie saw no conclusive act of insubordination on the "Somers," Capt. Vere did watch Billy strike Claggart dead.

3. Whereas the "Somers" episode took place on an American warship in time of peace during a contemporary period, the scene of *Billy Budd* was an English man-of-war sailing under battle orders, years before at the time of the French Revolution.

THE SPITHEAD AND NORE MUTINIES

To turn to other historical events that form part of the background of *Billy Budd,* there are the two famous English mutinies at Spithead and the Nore, which Melville mentions in the direct narrative of his novel and which Captain Vere speaks of in obvious terror when he justifies his action. Two passages of particular interest come from Edmund Fuller's book, in which he retells the story of these violent acts against authority.

The mutinies of 1797 were not a sudden outburst; there had been preliminary stirrings for some years. The mutiny of the "Bounty" was not perhaps directed solely against Bligh, but may be regarded also as a protest against the system. Even after the beginning of the Revolutionary War, single ship mutinies continued . . . . not particularly outstanding in themselves, they were straws which might have warned the authorities which way the wind was blowing, and have led them to reconsider the conditions under which the seamen were serving. Their significance, however, seems largely to have been missed, with the result that these small clouds ultimately united to produce a first-class storm just when it was least wanted. For the year 1797 was not a very promising one for England's cause in spite of the victories she had won at sea.

The other passage is closely related to the characterization in *Billy Budd:*

It is unfortunately only too obvious that a number of officers, at the time of the mutiny, were brutes of the first water —inhuman, inconsiderate, pitiless, and savage—and some of them gained promotion to command ships. They exercised no restraint, their brutality knew no limit, and unfortunately little official limit was put to their excesses. Some of the officers, however, who made large use of flogging, did so more out of narrow-mindedness than brutality. They thought it was the only way of maintaining discipline; it was the only thing the men would understand. The type still exists and is not, heaven knows, limited to the services, but is to be found in all walks of life. It may readily be imagined, however, that a ship commanded by either type, whether brutal or merely unimaginative, was a little floating hell with the Captain officiating as Satan and his subordinate officers (who would be morally bound to support him) as minor devils.

For the reader who remembers the essence of what Melville wrote in the preface of *Billy Budd,* it will be interesting to note that the result of the Spithead mutiny was that nearly one hundred officers, who were damned by their sailors for cruelty, were removed from their ships by order of the Admiralty.

Now, in view of the foregoing presentation of various kinds of background material—what might be called the environment of Melville's book—several important questions arise, almost inevitably: What kind of novel did Melville actually write? What sources did he use fact by fact, what did he leave out, and what did he change to suit his own design? Here is a special opportunity to understand and appreciate the book, since the reader meets the author not merely as a copyist, but as an inventor.

Even more important questions arise about moral ideas underlying the action of the novel. Is it actually, as some readers have said, immoral in its implications about good and evil? Most important, does it solve the conflict between man and the rules?

One thing is certain: long before the times were ready for it, Melville explored in profound detail and elaborate abstraction the problem of men's motives for their actions, especially those governed by strong emotion. This emphasis gives *Billy Budd* a psychological quality that is difficult to fathom even today, when readers and writers are steeped in such controversial tensions. There is no doubt that Melville stared, long and deeply, behind the rule of appearances, revealing that what men said about their motives and reasons could be contradicted by their manners and their actions.

Scholars, critics, and readers, nevertheless, are in great disagreement as to just what the novel solves by its treatment of ideas and its selection of actual events for the plot. Perhaps the only undebatable conclusion to be drawn is that Melville, in the face of general acquiescence to authority and rules and disregard of individual motives, included just the right material to cast dark shadows on the validity of this acquiescence.

Melville's undeclared purpose seems to have been to present, in the accepted manner of scientific investigation, all his ideas and his evidence, and then, as he said at one point in *Billy Budd,* leave the reader to determine the truth "for himself by such light as this narrative may afford."

PART FOUR

Billy Budd and *The Caine Mutiny*

It almost seems as if Herman Wouk read Melville's novel, and then said to himself: "I will write a book on the same subject and put in everything that Melville left out."

For the difference between these two stories of mutiny is in part a matter of mystery. What is ambiguous and abstract in Melville is blunt and concrete in Wouk; what is related at second hand in Melville is given in direct narrative in Wouk; and what Melville says the reader must figure out for himself, Wouk calls in professional psychiatrists to explain.

First, in its barest outline, Wouk's novel tells the story of a minesweeper in the Pacific during World War II. A long and painful series of incidents portrays, as in a movie, the growing antagonism between crew and captain, in which the captain is revealed in the worst possible light. Finally, at the height of a fierce typhoon, the executive officer, convinced that Captain Queeg is sick and disabled, takes command of the ship and saves it from capsizing. He is eventually tried by court-martial and acquitted, apparently on the ground that Queeg was incompetent. Later, however, the Navy issues a formal "reprimand," and it is clear at the end that the executive officer's career is finished.

Unlike Melville, Wouk expanded his story with minor plots, two in particular involving subordinate officers who are also in psychological distress. Also, in contrast to Melville's unidentified narrator, Wouk allows the reader to see much of his story through the eyes of a young lieutenant, who matures during the battle with his captain, but who remains a child throughout his sentimental affair with a nightclub singer.

One of the most striking contrasts between the two books involves the captains. Where it is barely suggested, in a few sentences, that Captain Vere might possibly be "unhinged," Wouk overwhelms the reader with detailed proof that Queeg was sick, physically and mentally. While at sea he is continually pictured as a nasty little man with pussy habits, and then during the court-martial he is systematically needled by the defense lawyer until he has no dignity left. Vere, on the contrary, is never subjected to such prolonged and obscene intimacy, and even in his controversial justification, is never ridiculous. These treatments have opposite effects on the reader's sympathies: one tends to be for Vere and against Queeg.

Another of Wouk's major "additions" is a clear picture of the previous lives of the main characters, so that the reader is flooded with specific moral and physical motives for their strange behavior. This is a vital matter of judgment; anyone who enjoys reading about characters who sound like the people next door may find Melville's novel too remote, abstract, and impersonal. The result is that Wouk's people appear victims of their merciless past lives, whereas Melville's suffer from traits that have no earthly origin, that are just there.

There is a sense of isolation in Melville's book, as if the author, like an experimental scientist, had focused out everything except the bones of the trouble. In *The Caine Mutiny* the reader is stuffed, not only with small detail but with the massive abstract issues too, so that at the end he feels as though he had been dragged through the whole catastrophe himself. This feeling is heightened by the long passages of intimate dialogue and the author's decision to write in every scene the reader could possibly want. Melville is older and more restrained, and probably his book appeals to a different audience.

And yet, weeks after reading the two books, the modern reader may realize that by different roads the authors arrive at similar disheartening conclusions. One is that in a con-

flict between individual and massive institution, the individual loses. At the end of Wouk's tale the two main characters who opposed the system, though alive and partly
cleared, are damned, frustrated men. In Melville's book,
the rebel is executed in disgrace.

Also, at the end the two books settle in the same way
the moral conflict between face-saving and justice. Billy is
hanged publicly for the good of the Navy, yet he was in
the "right"—innocent of mutiny, and the avenging angel
of his honor against the liar Claggart. Lieutenant Maryk
was ruined by the Navy after the court-martial, and yet
Wouk made it perfectly clear that he took command from
Queeg when the captain was frozen stiff with fear. Both
writers dramatize their humane morality.

This fact sharpens the ironic difference between "being there" at the time of a tragedy, and trying to explain
everything months later, with words. Both books—though
Wouk's is more fiercely dramatic and obviously moral—
leave the reader depressed by a kind of unconscious hypoc-
risy among the Monday-afternoon quarterbacks of tragedy.
The essence of the fault lies in righteous attempts, in the
aftermath, to force abstract rules down over embarrassing
deeds that won't shrink. Thus in a sense both books are
unfinished.

As a result of realizing how sad their stories were, I
think both writers closed by tacking up a faint hope. For
natural-born Americans this was nearly inevitable, since
ours was the land of the happy ending long before Holly-
wood tried to clinch it. On the last page Melville wrote a
sentimental ballad in the form of a monologue by Billy
just before his death. The effect is almost humorous and
soft, like all folksongs. "Written" by a fellow sailor after
the affair had settled, the ballad suggests that the men on
the *Indomitable* eventually calmed down and accepted the
tragedy with a kind of corn-fed resignation. The Moral?
"This too will pass."

On the last page of *The Caine Mutiny* Wouk's narrator,
now theoretically graduated from his college-boyishness
with a "P.G." course in world warfare, says he's going to
marry the girl. Wouk does not show the nuptial triumph

over evil, but, just like Dickens at the end of *Great Expectations,* he teases the reader with hopes of bliss.

Believable? "One must determine for himself by such light as this narrative may afford." Herman Melville in *Billy Budd,* page 60.

PART FIVE

Opinions, Reviews, and Comments

The following passages from professional discussions of Melville's novel reveal not only the writers' personal evaluations of the book, but the profound insights that it has given them into the nature of the world of man.

Differences in Evaluation [1]
JAMES E. MILLER, JR.

Criticism of *Billy Budd* has ranged as widely in its interpretation as has that great mass of writing on *Moby Dick*. Some critics have seen a retelling of the story of Christ that constitutes Melville's "testament of acceptance" after all the years of doubt and defiance. Others, interpreting it primarily as satire and irony, have seen a subtle diabolism at work throughout the story. Some have read the story as a commentary on the impersonality and essential brutality of the modern state, exacting death penalties of the innocent. Still others have found the tale an affirmation of the need, even at the risk of injustice, for society to protect itself and to assure order for the general welfare. It is not easy to sift the truth from all this conflicting comment, but an understanding of Melville's themes in his other works will help to clarify his meaning in *Billy Budd*.

Lack of Energy in the Novel [2]
LEWIS MUMFORD

Billy Budd, Melville's final novel, is not a full-bodied story; there is statement, commentary, illustration, just statement, wise commentary, apt illustration: what is lacking is an independent and living creation. The epithets themselves lack body AND colour: *Billy Budd* has nothing to compare with the description of boiling whale-oil in *Moby Dick*—"a wild Hindoo odour, like the left wing of the Day of Judgment."

[1] From *A Reader's Guide to Herman Melville*. The Noonday Press, a subsidiary of Farrar, Straus and Giroux, 1962.
[2] From *Herman Melville*. Harcourt, Brace and World, 1929.

Billy Budd . . . . lacks the fecundity and energy of *White Jacket:* the story itself takes place on the sea, but the sea itself is missing, and even the principal characters are not primarily men: they are actors and symbols. The story gains something by this concentration, perhaps: it is stripped for action, and even Melville's deliberate digressions do not halt it.

Great Lucidity in the Novel [3]
A. R. HUMPHREYS

Melville's last story is so lucid and thoughtful as to need little commentary; it is its own best expression of his mood in his last years. . . . We recognize again his lasting concerns—inscrutable Deity creating good and evil (yet here as in Shakespearean tragedy implicitly vindicating goodness); we recognize the mystery of wickedness . . . and the problems of private conscience and the public code, and of heavenly justice and earthly ("Struck dead by an angel of God. Yet the Angel must hang.") . . . .

Distanced by retrospection, the story gains in simplicity. The shipboard detail is simple but is not presented as in *White Jacket,* as an encyclopedia of naval life. The crew is real, but only as choric participants, surrounding the trio involved. Good and evil are to be observed in human nature, for which the social context is merely a frame, though a frame whose strong character provides the precise governing conditions. Among the finest things in Melville's work is the analysis of Claggart's mixed yearning and malice, real in its strangeness, given without the histrionics of Ahab. The analysis is probing, adumbrative, quietly troubled, and more interesting than any sensationalism could be. It presents, one might say, original sin according to agnosticism. The technical virtue of the moral enquiry is the degree to which it is embodied in the story. Not that Melville avoids conducting his own discussion; there is a good deal of commentary. But this all arises so fully from and so integrally in the narrative that idea, character, and event belong together. The morality is not a separable thing, and to import into criticism discussions of fallen and unfallen man, for instance, is to be too extraneous. One need not, as elsewhere, render the meaning down into terms other than its own. The story beautifully unites, with moved acceptance of fate, Melville's best fictional world (men at sea), his best manner (a rendering of life deeply sensed and judged), his best wis-

[3] From *Herman Melville*. Evergreen Books, the Grove Press, 1962.

dom (reverence for goodness in trouble), and his best meta-physical interest (spiritual power in its uncertain leaning to goodness).

Melville's Everlasting Yea [4]
JOHN FREEMAN

Like *Moby-Dick* this late and pure survival of Melville's genius has a double interest, the interest of story and the interest of psychology. *Billy Budd* is the narrative of one who, like Pierre, is unpracticed in the ways of life and the hates of other men; guilelessness is a kind of genius and the better part of innocence in this handsome young sailor. . . .

Exaltation of spirit redeems such a scene [as the hanging scene] from burdens which otherwise might appear too painful to be borne. And beyond this, it is innocence that is vindicated, more conspicuously in death than it could be in life. . . . The ultimate opposition is shown clearly . . . in this public vindication of the law, and the superior assertion at the very moment of death of the nobility of pure human spirit. *Moby-Dick* ends in darkness and desolation, for the challenge of Ahab's pride is rebuked by the physical power and the unhumanness of Nature; but *Billy Budd* ends in a brightness of escape, such as the apostle saw when he exclaimed, "Death, where is thy sting!"

Finished but a few months before the author's death and only lately published, *Billy Budd* shows the imaginative faculty still secure and powerful, after nearly forty years' supineness, and the not less striking security of Melville's inward peace. . . . In his last days he reenters an Eden-like sweetness and serenity . . . and sets his brief, appealing tragedy for witness that evil is defeat and natural goodness invincible in the affections of man. In this, the simplest of stories, told with but little of the old digressive vexatiousness, and based upon recorded incidents, Herman Melville uttered his everlasting yea, and died before a soul had been allowed to hear him.

An Unconventional Interpretation [5]
LAWRANCE THOMPSON

In his patient writing and rewriting of *Billy Budd*, Melville finally achieved that quality of artistic detachment which he had sought to achieve in each of his narratives, starting with *Mardi*. This time, with seeming effortlessness, he handles a

[4] From *Herman Melville*. The Macmillan Company, 1926.
[5] From *Melville's Quarrel with God*. Princeton University Press, 1952.

complex artistic formula which combines, ingeniously, sustained irony and sustained (but inverted) allegory. The artistic effect amounts to a new variation of the Melvillian triple-talk, because it makes discrete appeals to three distinct viewpoints.

An unsophisticated and superficial skimmer of pages might be willing to settle for the mere story concerning the impressment of a sailor and the subsequent hanging of that sailor because he strikes and kills a superior.

A second viewpoint, represented by any reader who is biased by his Christian heritage (whether he acknowledges it or not) is slyly encouraged by Melville to take the story as a sort of morality play which dramatizes the tragic conflict between good and evil in human experience.

A third viewpoint, represented by any reader who can transcend the bias of his own prejudices, is slyly encouraged by Melville to view the story as a bitter comedy, in the satiric and sarcastic tradition of Lucian and Voltaire and Tom Paine.

Naturally, the first and second categories of reader are inclined to be shocked at the mere suggestion that either the action or the narrative manner in *Billy Budd* could possibly be described as amusing or comic, in any sense: they see nothing there to laugh at. If such readers understand the traditional principles of satiric literary art, they should have no difficulty in overcoming their bias enough to recognize that the misanthropic Melville does indeed ask the reader to laugh with him, derisively, even to the bitter end of *Billy Budd*.

Part of Melville's deception, in *Billy Budd*, rests on his assurance that most readers forget one point: the comic or non-comic values of a situation (in literature or in life) depend entirely on the scale of values implicit in a spectator's viewpoint.

.   .   .   .

Melville's narrative method, in *Billy Budd*, involves the technical principle of sustained irony because Melville cunningly and slyly creates the artistic illusion that the narrator sympathizes, throughout, with the authoritarian viewpoint of Captain Vere, and praises Vere's actions, even though these actions are at several points palpably unpraiseworthy. This technical device might be described in another way: Melville gives the illusion of creating a narrator who is, in a sense, a character whom we as readers get to know because his remarks are self-revealing. Like the narrator in *The Confidence-Man*, this contrived narrator speaks from an essentially Christian viewpoint; but Melville arranges to let us see that the narrator is, at the same time, just a wee bit stupid.

. . . .

Billy himself represents the response which might be made by one category of reader: he perceives very little and does not even understand what he observes. The situation is differently evaluated by a second category of observer: the "harder faces" among the sailors wear an "ambiguous smile" when they look at Handsome Billy because they see something simultaneously pathetic and funny in impressing such an innocent into such an evil atmosphere. Thirdly, the situation is differently evaluated by the officers, who like Billy because he promises to be amenable. Now consider what happens if we imagine how the "harder faces" of the enlisted men evaluate the reactions of the officers to Billy: these enlisted men view the officers as liking Billy because the officers can play Billy for a sucker, so to speak. Melville's viewpoint, as represented in the larger context of the narrative, is represented by the "harder faces" of the enlisted men; but notice that Melville's contrived narrator would seem to be siding with the officers, whom he politely refers to as "the more intelligent gentlemen." More intelligent than whom? The referent is indefinite and so the effect is in accord with Melville's fondness for ambiguity.

In an early part of the novel, Melville wrote the following brief comment on Billy's stutter, which was so severe during emotional strain that he couldn't speak when Claggart lied about him. Instead he struck and killed the master-at-arms.

Under sudden provocation, Billy was apt to develop an organic hesitancy,—in fact, more or less of a stutter or even worse. In this particular Billy was a striking instance that the arch-interferer, the envious marplot of Eden, still has more or less to do with every human consignment to this planet . . .

Mr. Thompson's unusual interpretation of this passage is as follows:

The narrator, speaking from the Christian viewpoint, makes an orthodox application. . . . Satan is the "arch-interferer, the envious marplot of Eden." But consider the ambiguous Melvillian meaning. . . . He represents Billy's "defect" (which will eventually be responsible for his "sin" and con-

sequently responsible for his punishment by death) as an
"original" blemish or birthmark from Nature, or (allegorically
considered) a gift from God, his Maker. In this anti-Christian
context, God might be viewed as the responsible source of this
defect, this depravity, this sin, this death; God might be viewed
as the "arch interferer, the envious marplot of Eden."

Robert Frost's Reaction

Mr. Thompson's idea has aroused general disagreement
among students of Melville; but he had one impressive
agreement—in a letter he received from Robert Frost:

One look at your book and I should be sure that if they (the
reviewers) disagreed with you materially they were wrong. I
have encountered in the flesh . . . two or three of the party
of "acceptance" in the explanation of Billy Budd. They have
sounded to me sadistically foolish in their enjoyment of the
inexorable they never experienced except in literature. Of
course Melville hated God every step of the way in doing
Billy in. You did a great chapter there.

•   •   •   •   •   •   •   •   •   •   •   •

That's an awful story really. I think it the worst outrage
ever written. The purpose couldn't be anything but to dis-
credit God. But I am glad you take the position that Melville's
wrongness, unsoundness or whatever we call it matters next to
nothing at all in our judgment of him as a great story teller,
one of America's splendors in art.

Amherst, May 1952

Biblical References

Most powerful, according to some critics, are the Biblical references, direct and indirect. Here is one significant
interpretation, from James Miller's book *A Reader's Guide
to Herman Melville:*

Almost invariably Melville has described his Titanic heroes
as stricken Christs, but with none has the analogy been so
complete as with Billy Budd. From beginning to end, Christ
is the dominant metaphor of the story. When Billy is brought
aboard the H. M. S. INDOMITABLE in 1797, shortly after

the Great Mutiny which had rocked the British fleet, he is the epitome of innocence. Asked the routine questions—where was he born, who was his father—he replies, significantly, "God knows, Sir." His reputation, borne out by his behavior aboard ship, is that of a peacemaker, one who can miraculously transfigure hate and hostility into admiration and love. When Billy stands falsely accused before his Captain and cannot speak, his expression is "a crucifixion to behold." And when he kills his accuser with one blow, his Captain mutters, "Struck dead by an angel of God." Billy's last words before he hangs are—"God bless Captain Vere." And even after his death (or ascension), his "legend" lives on, and the spar from which he was hanged becomes sacred: "to sailors a chip of it was as a piece of the Cross."

But Billy is much more complex than simply a duplicate of Christ. Christ-like, yes, but also like Adam—Adam before the Fall: "Billy in many respects was little more than a sort of upright barbarian, much such perhaps as Adam presumably might have been ere the urbane Serpent wriggled himself into his company." Captain Vere congratulates his officers on gaining Billy, "such a fine specimen of the genus homo who, in the nude might have posed for a statue of young Adam before the fall." In his character and his appearance, Billy is an Adam as well as a Christ. The main import of this figure is that it emphasizes Billy's ignorance of evil: unlike Christ's, Billy's innocence is compounded, like Adam's before he ate the fruit, of his lack of knowledge of good and evil, and not of a profound insight into the nature of the world and man.

Finally, the following paragraphs from a review of the movie *Billy Budd* are informative, not only for comments about the movie itself, but for comparisons with Melville's novel. It was written by Pauline Kael for the magazine *Film Quarterly*, Spring, 1963.

In the film version of *Billy Budd*, Melville's story has been stripped for action; and I think this was probably the right method—the ambiguities of the story probably come through more clearly than if the film were not so straightforward in its narrative line. The very cleanness of the narrative method, Peter Ustinov's efficient direction, Robert Krasker's stylized, controlled photography, help to release the meanings. The film could easily have been clogged by metaphysical speculation and homo-erotic overtones. Instead, it is a good, tense movie that doesn't try to tell us too much—and so gives us a very great deal.

Unfortunately, the role of Captain Vere as played by Ustinov is a serious misconception that weakens the film, particularly in the last section. Ustinov gives a fine performance but it doesn't belong in the story of Billy Budd: it reduces the meanings to something clear-cut and banal. Ustinov's physical presence is all wrong; his warm, humane, sensual face turns Melville's Starry Vere into something like a cliche of the man who wants to do the right thing, the liberal. We *believe* him when he presents his arguments about justice and law!

Perhaps it is Ustinov's principles that have prevented him from seeing farther into Melville's equivocations. Ustinov has explained that he was concerned "with a most horrible situation where people are compelled by the letter of the law, which is archaic, to carry out sentences which they don't wish to do. That obviously produces a paradox which is tragic." This is, no doubt, an important subject for Ustinov, but it is not the kind of paradox that interested Melville. Melville, so plagued by Billy Budd that he couldn't get it in final form (he was still revising it when he died), had far more unsettling notions of its content.

As Ustinov presents the film, the conflict is between the almost abstract forces of good (Billy) and evil (Claggart) with the captain a human figure tragically torn by the rules and demands of authority. Obviously. But what gives the story its fascination, its greatness, is the ambivalent Captain; and there is nothing in Ustinov's performance, or in his conception of the story, to suggest the unseemly haste with which Vere tries to hang Billy. In Melville's account the other officers can't understand why Vere doesn't simply put Billy in confinement "in a way dictated by usage and postpone further action in so extraordinary a case to such time as they should again join the squadron, and then transfer it to the admiral." The surgeon thinks the Captain must be "suddenly affected in his mind." Melville's Vere, who looks at the dead Claggart and exclaims, "Struck dead by an angel of God. Yet the angel must hang!" is not so much a tragic victim of the law as he is Claggart's master and a distant relative perhaps of the Grand Inquisitor. Sweet Starry Vere is the evil we CAN'T detect: the man whose motives and conflicts we can't fathom. Claggart we can spot, but he is merely the underling doing the Captain's work: it is the Captain, Billy's friend, who continues the logic by which saints must be destroyed.

PART SIX

Herman Melville: A Biographical Sketch

In almost every way, the boyhood and early maturity of Herman Melville were unlike the lives of contemporary American high-school students. He had no regular schooling, no organized athletics, no boy-girl "mixers," and no fast vehicles to race around the countryside looking for action. Furthermore, he lived amid constant tension at home because his father was an unstable character who couldn't support his family—a family of eight children growing up in New York City, where they tried to appear better off than they really were.

To make matters worse, there was considerable illness in the family, most unfortunately in the case of the oldest brother, on whom the family depended for their economic and social future. Nobody, apparently, had much confidence in Herman, for he was not aggressive. Since in the early part of the 19th century no girls ever did any work, the four sisters were a complete financial liability.

When Herman was nine, his father's business failed and the family moved to Albany, hoping to find less expensive living arrangements and a new job. Nothing, however, worked out, and Melville's father drove himself so hard and so foolishly that he destroyed his own health. When Herman was thirteen and just starting a real education, his father suffered a total nervous breakdown and died without ever understanding what happened. The family was left nearly penniless and without much outside help, since the closest relatives were also in financial trouble.

Throughout all this mess of bad luck, Herman kept control of himself, both physically and mentally, and went to work as a clerk in a local bank at the age of thirteen. For several years the family scraped along, helped out by

gifts from friends in Boston, and then the whole country
was devastated by the financial panic of 1837. With all
kinds of business shrinking, Herman tried teaching school
for a few months, and then dabbled at writing for a local
newspaper. But these efforts led to nothing profitable, and
the family situation grew so embarrassing that they were
forced to move into a small village to reduce expenses.

Finally, in the spring of 1839, when Melville was twenty,
he found the tensions at home so great and the prospects
of a job so hopeless that he decided to go to sea, as some
people today go into the army. He obtained a job as a
common sailor on a merchant vessel, and took off for
England.

This was the first of several long trips on the ocean,
which eventually provided Melville with much of the subject matter that dominated his books. He learned the
minute details of a sailor's harsh life, he encountered for
the first time the rigid, cold authority of dictatorial captains, and he worked with bizarre characters who later
became the people of his stories.

When he came home from this first voyage, he found
the situation in his family even worse. This time he took
the traditional American advice to "go West," hoping that
even in a depression year the magic might work and produce a job. But again there was nothing.

His next voyage lasted four years—a whaling trip to
the South Pacific. Here he had the specific, dramatic experiences that led to the writing of seven novels in eight
years, after he returned in 1844 at the age of 24: *Typee,*
1846; *Omoo,* 1847; *Mardi,* 1849; *Redburn,* 1849; *White
Jacket,* 1850; *Moby Dick,* 1851; and *Pierre,* 1852. He
saw whaling from the handle of a harpoon, took part in a
small mutiny, jumped ship and lived with "cannibals" for
several weeks (carefully scrutinizing their "leftovers"),
observed the American missionaries trying to convert na-
tives in Hawaii, served on a United States warship, and
suffered the torment of watching more than a hundred
sailors flogged.

When he came home he was so full of events, ideas,
images and emotions that he began furiously to write.

Eventually his wife and children suffered from the intensity of this creative activity, for Melville became a dedicated professional, and while working on his books, often locked himself in his room for hours in order to concentrate on reading, thinking, and writing. Now and then he did take time off for social life, and in the spring and summer successfully cultivated a garden, to help his family survive.

But Melville in these years was essentially a writer's writer, and most of his time was spent with books and literary men, particularly Nathaniel Hawthorne, who inspired him profoundly during the composition of his masterpiece, *Moby Dick*. He read constantly and widely, and in many instances, when his own imagination let him down, rewrote material from other books into his own.

Thus it must have been a frightening and disillusioning shock for Melville to realize, in the years immediately following the publication of *Pierre* when he was thirty-three, that he had virtually written himself out, and that on the basis of the few pieces he turned out after this novel, he could not support his family as a writer. He tried a few short stories, did some minor magazine work, went out on a futile lecture tour, and then, at the age of forty-eight, under pressure from his family to give up, he finally took a job as a customs inspector in New York. For nearly a quarter of a century he lived in respectable economic security, but never again published a book of any importance. Though he worked a little at composing poetry, it was clearly not as a professional writer.

Finally, in the last year of his life, he felt compelled to write one more book, which is the basis for this volume, *Billy Budd*. Yet he never made a final manuscript, and the book did not appear until 1924. Now Melville has been rediscovered, and his work is being read, studied, and analyzed as being among the greatest this country has produced.

Melville's greatness rests upon the ideas and events that inspired him as a writer—dramatic, intellectual, and moral questions of eternal value: man's cruelty to other men, the conflict between individuals and institutions, the problem of good and evil, the psychological and, sometimes, psychiatric reasons for men's actions, the differences between physical reality and hidden truth, and the discoveries a man makes traveling to outlandish countries. He did not answer these problems clearly and satisfactorily, but he opened men's minds to certain kinds of conflict that in his time few people wanted to face realistically.

Principal Works of Herman Melville

Typee: A Peep at Polynesian Life	1846
Omoo	1847
Mardi and a Voyage Thither	1849
Redburn: His First Voyage	1849
White Jacket	1850
Moby Dick	1851
Pierre	1852
Piazza Tales	1855
The Confidence Man	1857
Battle-Pieces and Aspects of the War	1866
Clarel	1876
Billy Budd, Foretopman	1891